C000142182

RIFFS & RHYTHMS

ROCK ANTHEMS

UNIQUE, EASY TO FOLLOW FORMAT
39 ROCK HITS FROM THE BIGGEST ARTISTS
SPECIALLY PRESENTED FOR GUITARISTS

WISE PUBLICATIONS
PART OF THE MUSIC SALES GROUP
LONDON / NEW YORK / PARIS / SYDNEY / COPENHAGEN / BERLIN / MADRID / TOKYO

PUBLISHED BY
WISE PUBLICATIONS
14-15 BERNERS STREET, LONDON W1T 3LJ, UK.

EXCLUSIVE DISTRIBUTORS:
MUSIC SALES LIMITED
DISTRIBUTION CENTRE, NEWMARKET ROAD,
BURY ST EDMUNDS, SUFFOLK IP33 3YB, UK.
MUSIC SALES PTY LIMITED
120 ROTHSCHILD AVENUE,
ROSEBERY, NSW 2018, AUSTRALIA.

ORDER NO. AM985149
ISBN 978-1-84609-470-5
THIS BOOK © COPYRIGHT 2007 WISE PUBLICATIONS,
A DIVISION OF MUSIC SALES LIMITED.

EDITED BY DAVID HARRISON
COMPILED BY NICK CRISPIN
MUSIC ARRANGED BY MATT COWE
MUSIC PROCESSED BY PAUL EWERS MUSIC DESIGN
COVER DESIGNED BY FRESH LEMON
COVER PHOTOGRAPHS COURTESY OF LFI
PRINTED IN THE EU

20TH CENTURY BOY

Words & Music by Marc Bolan

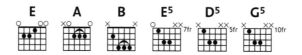

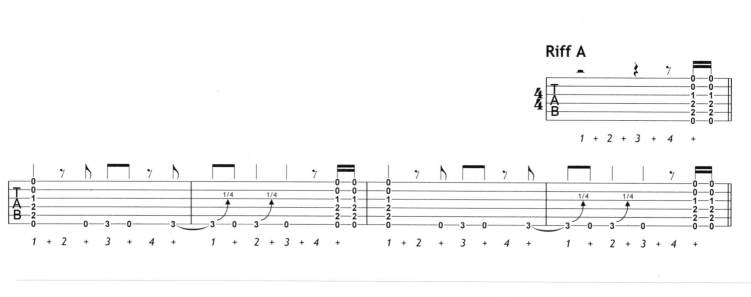

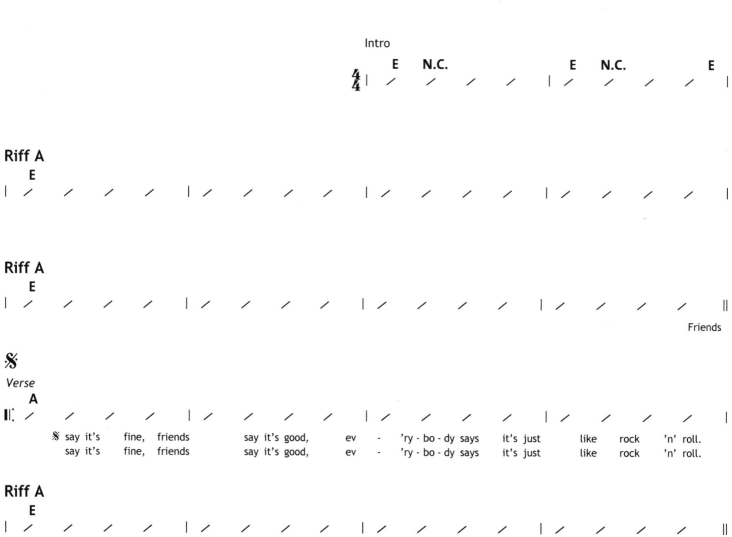

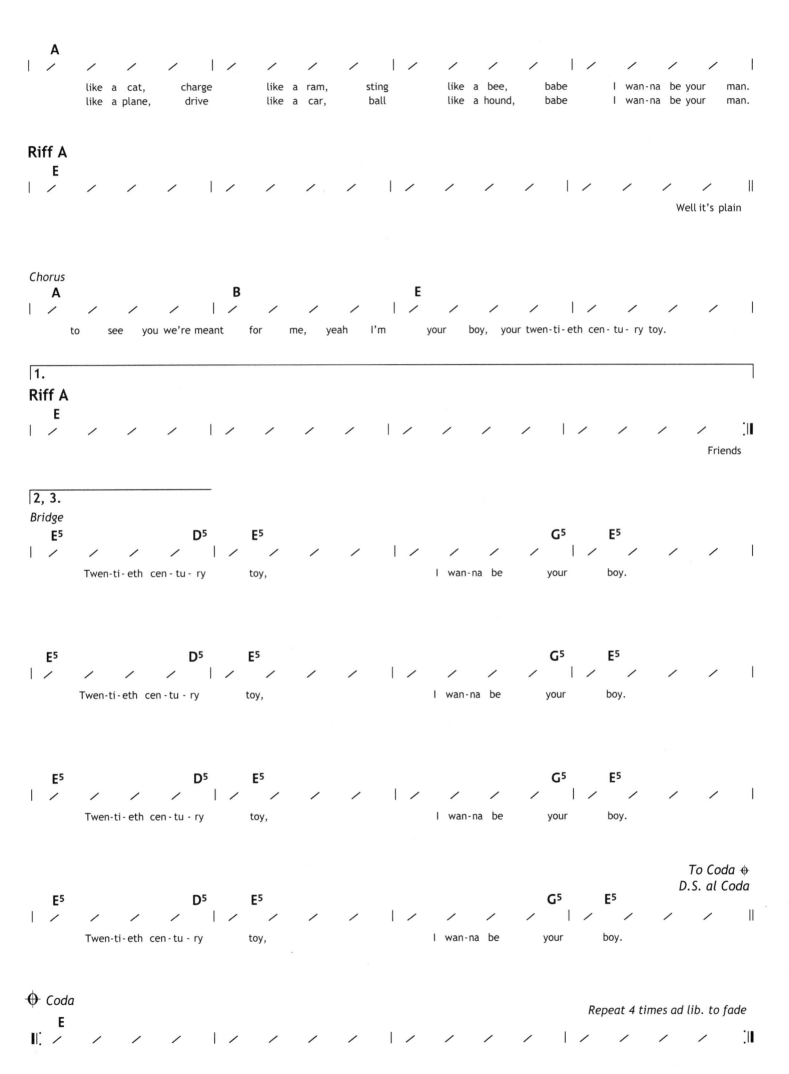

A

like a cat,　charge　like a ram,　sting　like a bee,　babe　I wan-na be your man.
like a plane,　drive　like a car,　ball　like a hound,　babe　I wan-na be your man.

Riff A

E

Well it's plain

Chorus

A　　　　　　　　**B**　　　　　**E**

to　see　you we're meant　for　me,　yeah I'm　your　boy, your twen-ti-eth cen-tu-ry toy.

|1.

Riff A

E

Friends

|2, 3.

Bridge

E⁵　　　　　**D⁵**　**E⁵**　　　　　　　　　**G⁵**　**E⁵**

Twen-ti-eth cen-tu-ry　　toy,　　　I wan-na be　　your　boy.

E⁵　　　　　**D⁵**　**E⁵**　　　　　　　　　**G⁵**　**E⁵**

Twen-ti-eth cen-tu-ry　　toy,　　　I wan-na be　　your　boy.

E⁵　　　　　**D⁵**　**E⁵**　　　　　　　　　**G⁵**　**E⁵**

Twen-ti-eth cen-tu-ry　　toy,　　　I wan-na be　　your　boy.

To Coda ⊕
D.S. al Coda

E⁵　　　　　**D⁵**　**E⁵**　　　　　　　　　**G⁵**　**E⁵**

Twen-ti-eth cen-tu-ry　　toy,　　　I wan-na be　　your　boy.

⊕ *Coda*

Repeat 4 times ad lib. to fade

E

5

ALIVE

Words & Music by Marcos Curiel, Mark Daniels, Paul Sandoval & Noah Bernardo

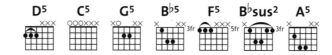

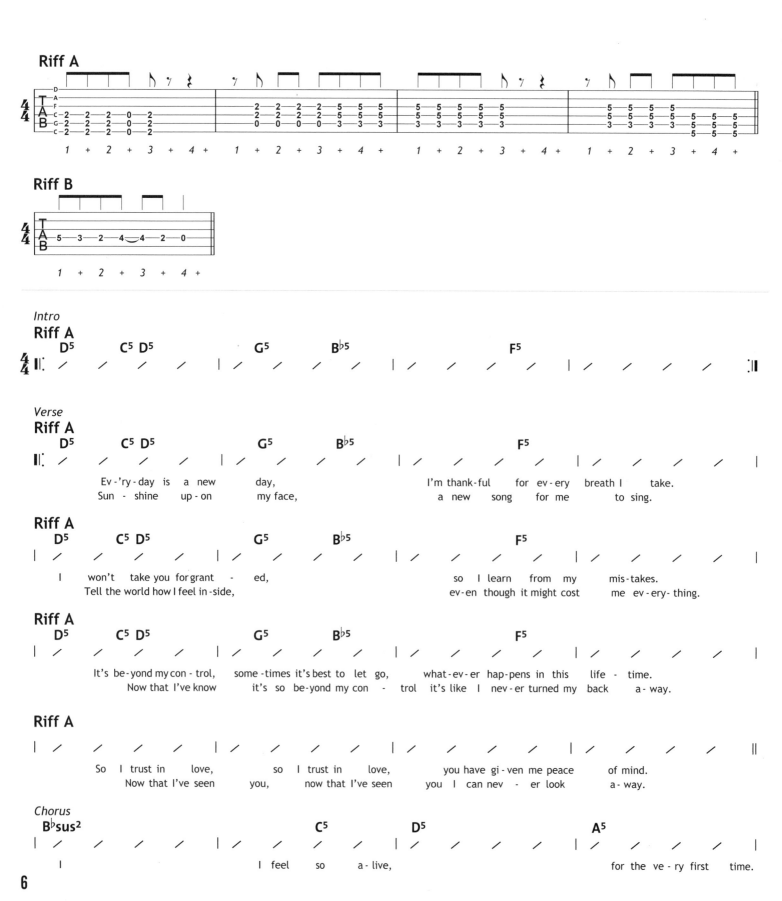

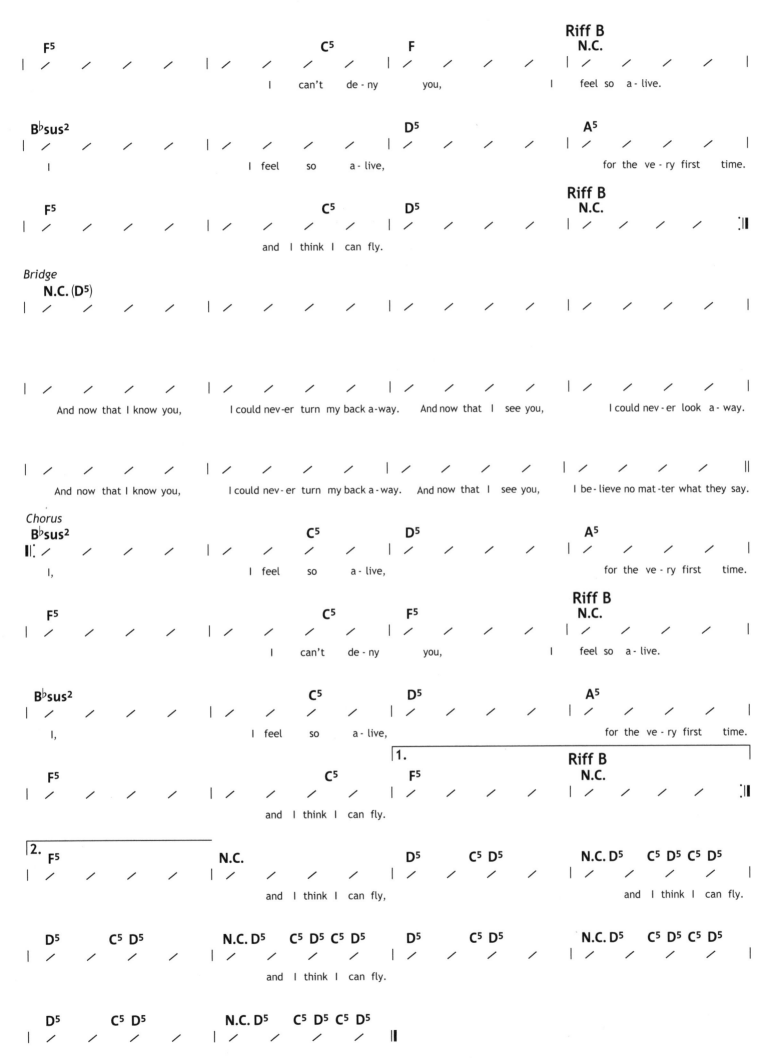

ALL ALONG THE WATCHTOWER

Words & Music by Bob Dylan

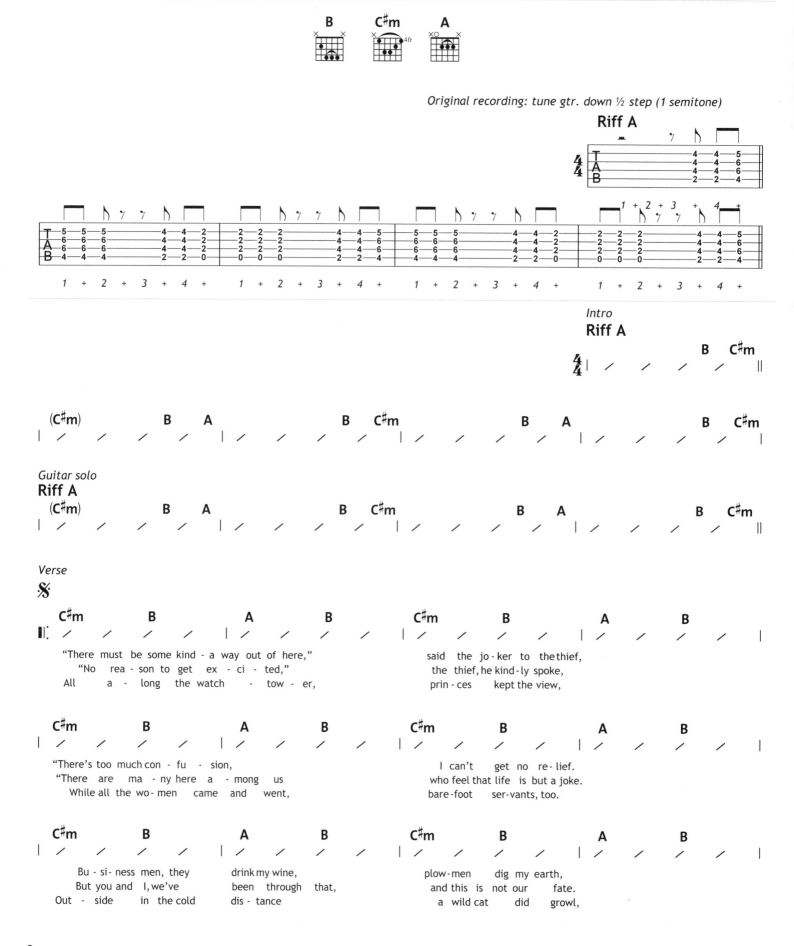

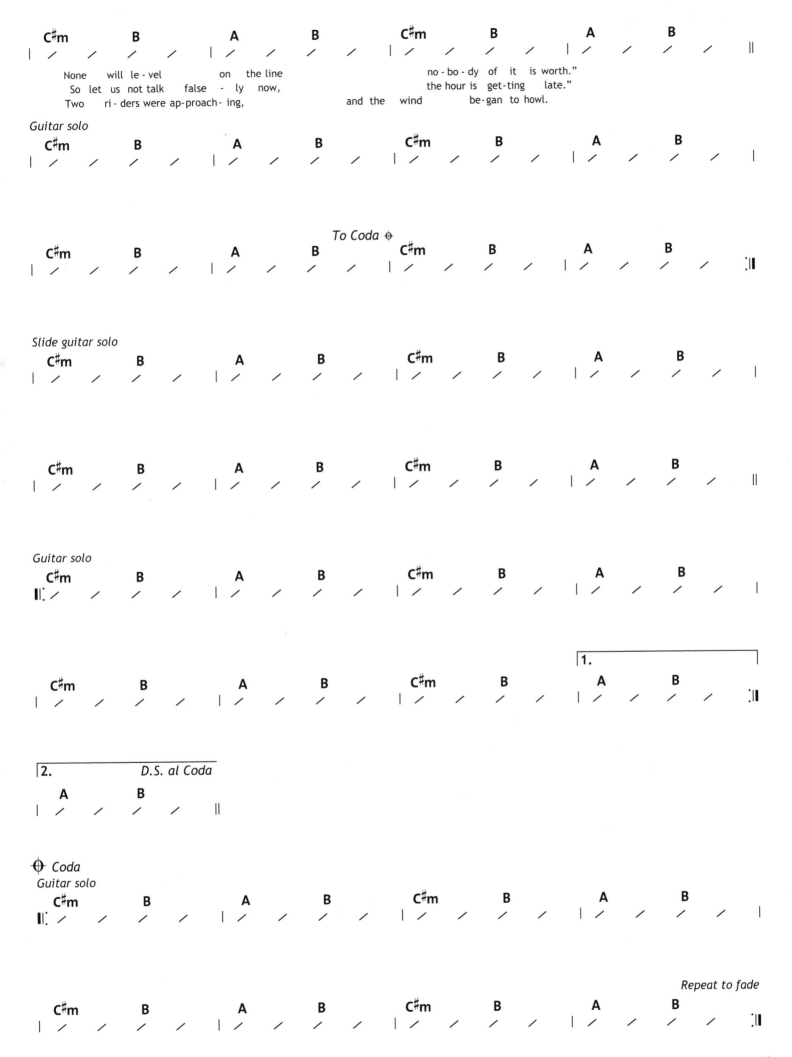

None   will le - vel   on the line   no - bo - dy of it is worth."
So let us not talk   false - ly now,   the hour is get-ting   late."
Two   ri - ders were ap-proach- ing,   and the wind   be-gan to howl.

Guitar solo

Slide guitar solo

Guitar solo

1.

2.   *D.S. al Coda*

✦ *Coda*
Guitar solo

Repeat to fade

ALL RIGHT NOW

Words & Music by Paul Rodgers & Andy Fraser

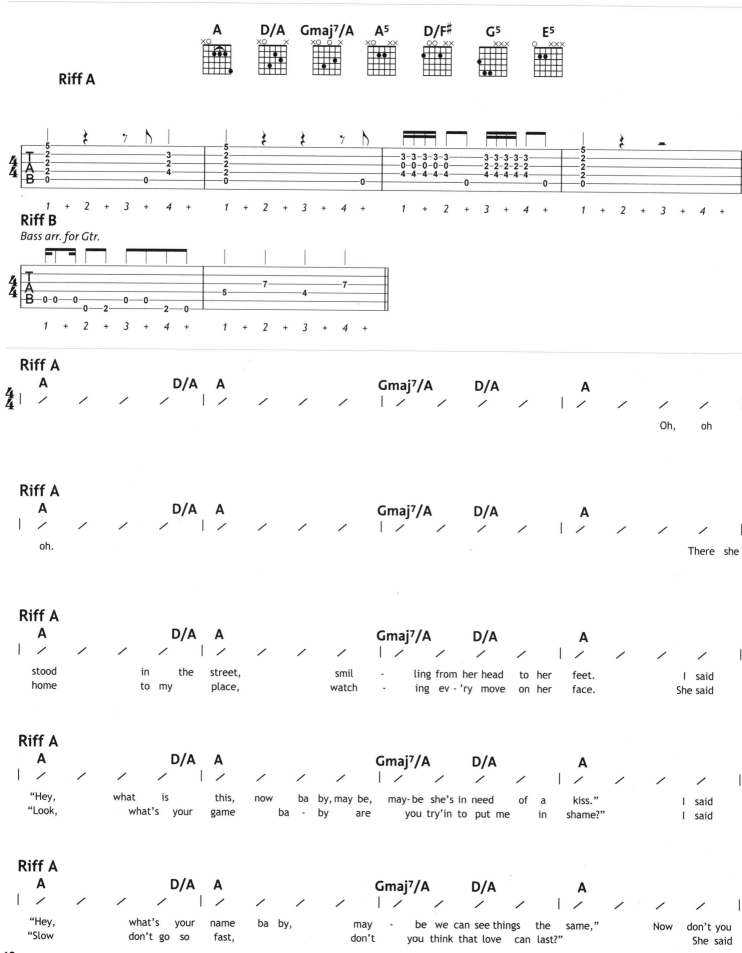

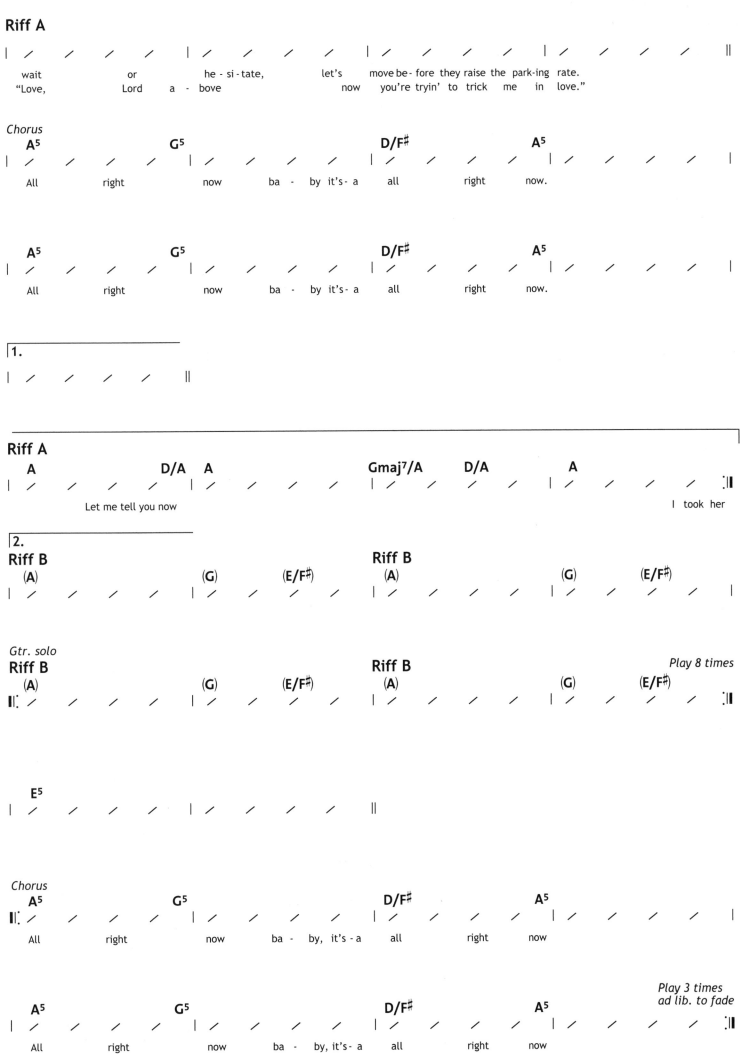

AIN'T TALKIN' 'BOUT LOVE

Words & Music by Edward Van Halen, Alex Van Halen, Michael Anthony & David Lee Roth

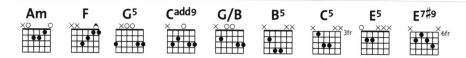

Original recording: tune gtr. down whole step (1 tone)

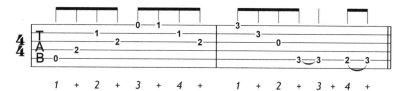

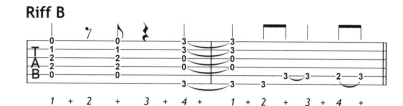

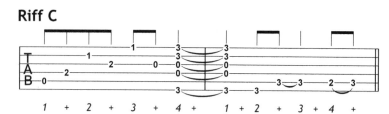

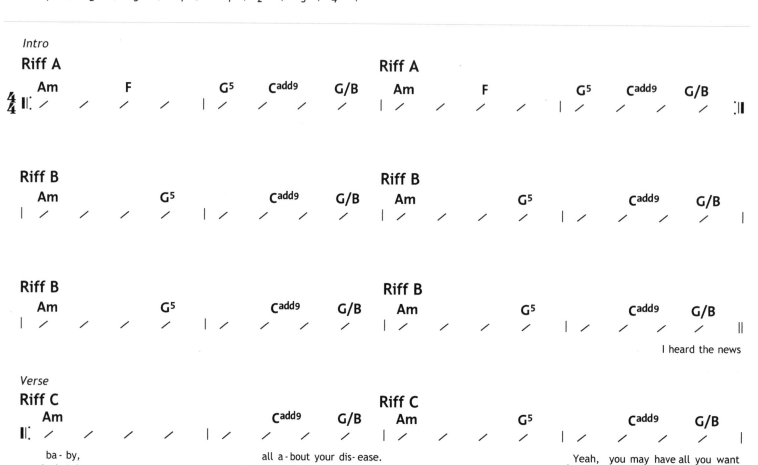

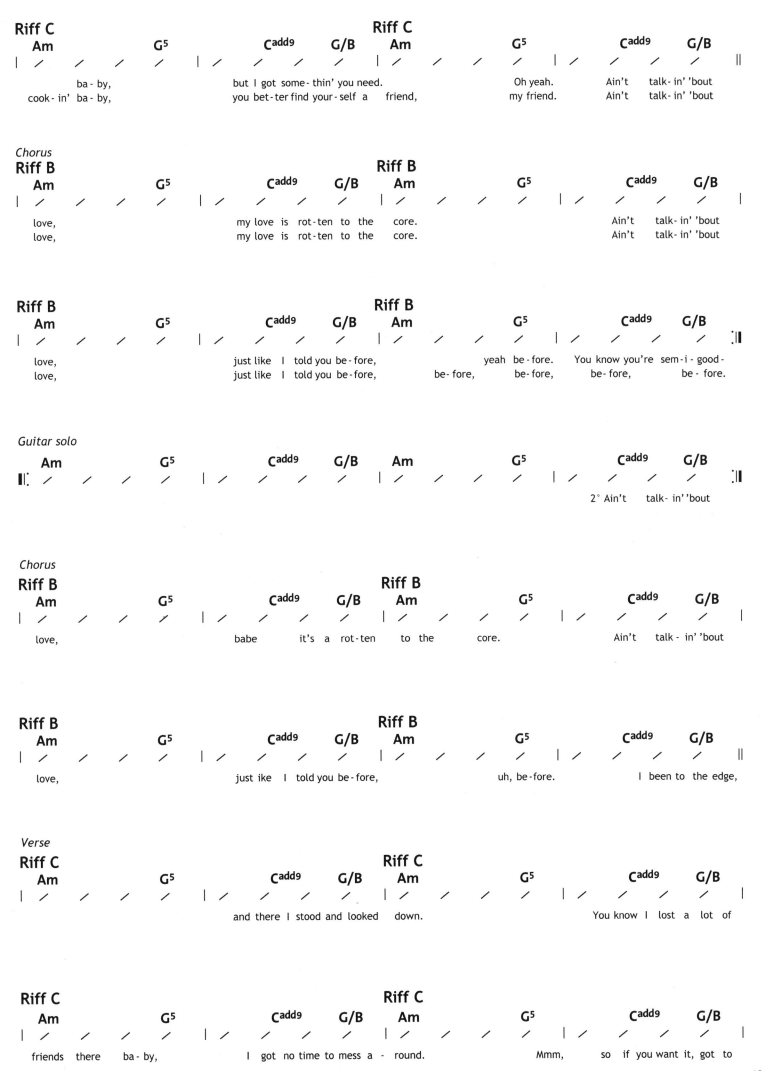

Riff C
Am   G⁵   Cadd9   G/B   **Riff C** Am   G⁵   Cadd9   G/B

cook- in' ba - by,   but I got some- thin' you need.   Oh yeah.   Ain't   talk- in' 'bout
ba - by,   you bet-ter find your-self a   friend,   my friend.   Ain't   talk- in' 'bout

Chorus
Riff B
Am   G⁵   Cadd9   G/B   **Riff B** Am   G⁵   Cadd9   G/B

love,   my love is rot-ten to the   core.   Ain't   talk- in' 'bout
love,   my love is rot-ten to the   core.   Ain't   talk- in' 'bout

Riff B
Am   G⁵   Cadd9   G/B   **Riff B** Am   G⁵   Cadd9   G/B

love,   just like I told you be-fore,   yeah be-fore. You know you're sem-i-good-
love,   just like I told you be-fore,   be-fore,   be-fore,   be-fore,   be-fore.

Guitar solo
Am   G⁵   Cadd9   G/B   Am   G⁵   Cadd9   G/B

2° Ain't   talk- in' 'bout

Chorus
Riff B
Am   G⁵   Cadd9   G/B   **Riff B** Am   G⁵   Cadd9   G/B

love,   babe   it's a rot-ten   to the   core.   Ain't   talk- in' 'bout

Riff B
Am   G⁵   Cadd9   G/B   **Riff B** Am   G⁵   Cadd9   G/B

love,   just ike I told you be-fore,   uh, be-fore.   I been to the edge,

Verse
Riff C
Am   G⁵   Cadd9   G/B   **Riff C** Am   G⁵   Cadd9   G/B

and there I stood and looked   down.   You know I lost a lot of

Riff C
Am   G⁵   Cadd9   G/B   **Riff C** Am   G⁵   Cadd9   G/B

friends there ba - by,   I got no time to mess a - round.   Mmm,   so if you want it, got to

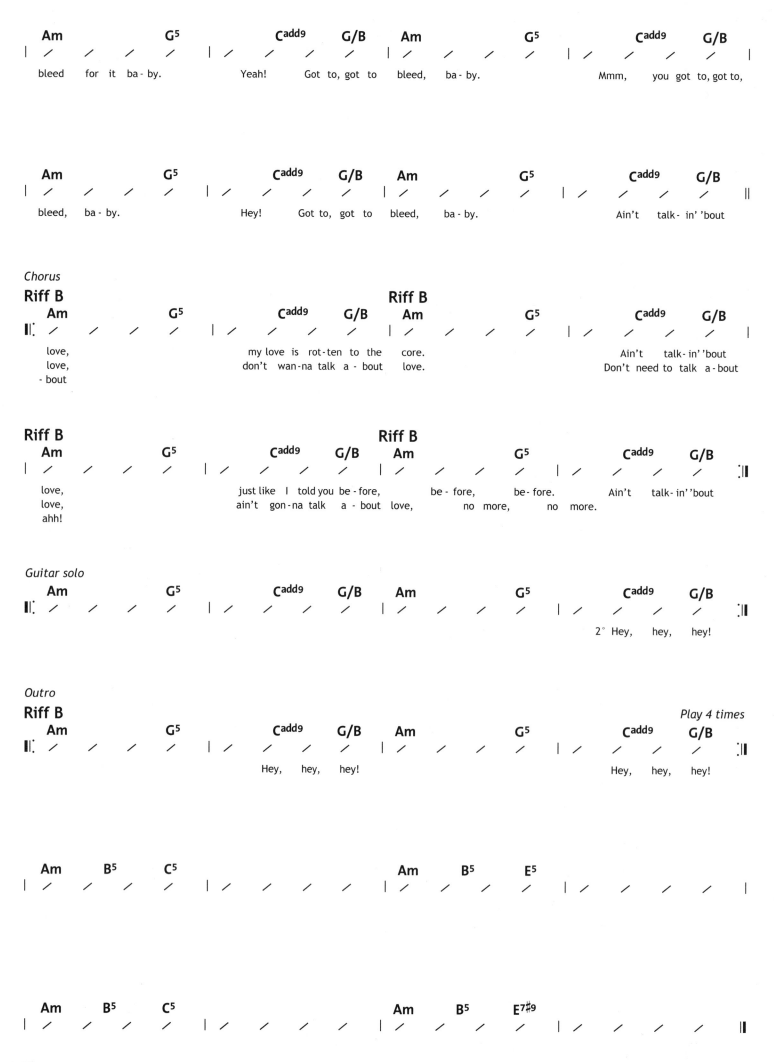

14

B.Y.O.B.

Words & Music by Serj Tankian & Daron Malakian

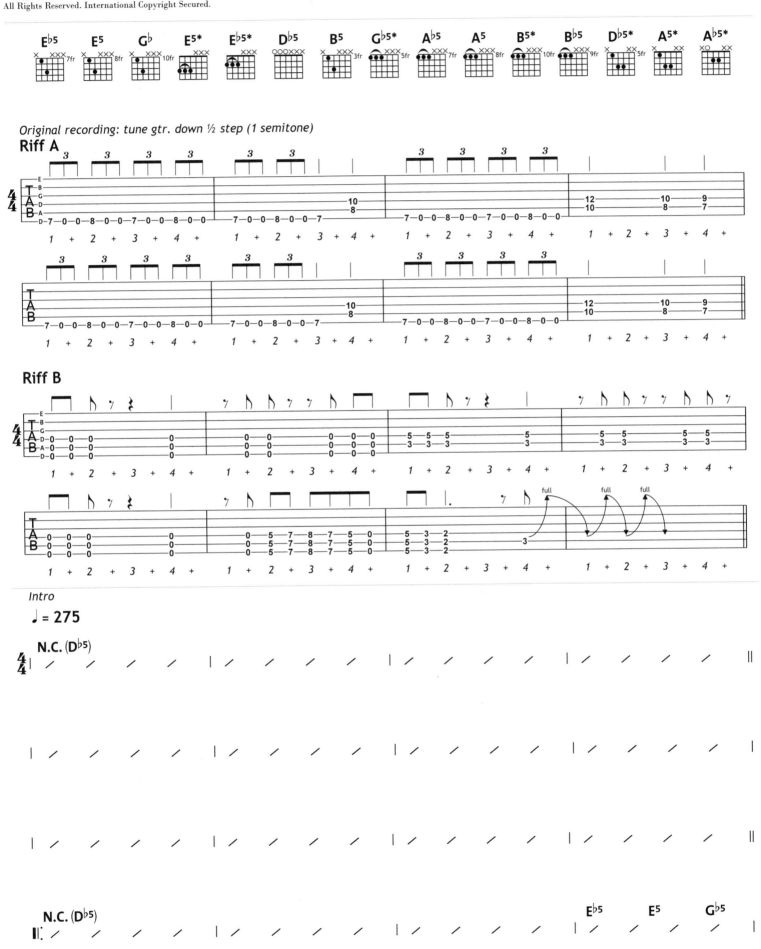

N.C. (D♭5)　　　　　　　　　　　　　　　　　　　　　　G♭5　　E5　　E♭5

♩ = 190

N.C.

Why　do they al - ways　send　the poor?

%

Verse
Riff A

N.C.　　　　　　　　　　　　　E5　　N.C.　　　　　　G♭5　　　E5　E♭5

Ba - ba - ri - sms　by　Bar - ba - ra　with　point - ed　heels.
(%) Knee - ing　ro - ses　dis - ap - pear - ing　in - to　Mo - ses - 's　dry　mouth.

N.C.　　　　　　　　　　　　　E5　　N.C.　　　　　　G♭5　　　E5　E♭5

Vic - to - ri - ous　vic - to - ries　kneel　for　brand　new　spank - ing　deals.
Break - ing　in - to　Fort　Knox　steal - ing　our　in - ten - tions.

Riff A

N.C.　　　　　　　　　　　　　E5　　N.C.　　　　　　G♭5　　　E5　E♭5

March - ing　for - ward　hyp - o - cri - tic　and　hyp - no - tic　com - pu - ters.
Han - gars sit - ing　dripped　in oil　cry - ing　freedom!

N.C.　　　　　　　　　　　　　E5　　N.C.　　　　　　G♭5*　　　E5*

You　de - pend　on　our　pro - tec - tion,　yet　you　feed　us　lies　from　the
Hand - ed　to　ob - so - le - tion,　still　you　feed　us　lies　from　the

Bridge
G♭5* E5*D♭5　　　　　　E♭5* E5 G♭5*A♭5 E♭5*D♭5 E5* E♭5*B5　　　　　N.C.

ta - ble cloth.)
ta - ble cloth.)

G♭5* E5*D♭5　　　　　　E♭5* E5 G♭5*A♭5 E♭5*D♭5 E5* E♭5*B5　　　　　N.C.

La la la la la la la　la la la.　Ooh.

Chorus
Riff B

D♭5　　　　　　　　　　　　B5

Ev - 'ry - bo - dy's　go - ing to　the　par - ty, have　a　real　good

D♭5　　　　　　　　　　G♭5A♭5 A5 A♭5G♭5D♭5　G♭5 E5 E♭5

time.

Riff B

D♭5　　　　　　　　　　　　B5

Danc - ing in　the　de - sert,　blow - ing up　the　sun -

D♭5　　　　　　　　　　G♭5A♭5 A5 A♭5G♭5D♭5　G♭5 E5 E♭5

- shine.

BACK IN BLACK

Words & Music by Angus Young, Malcolm Young & Brian Johnson

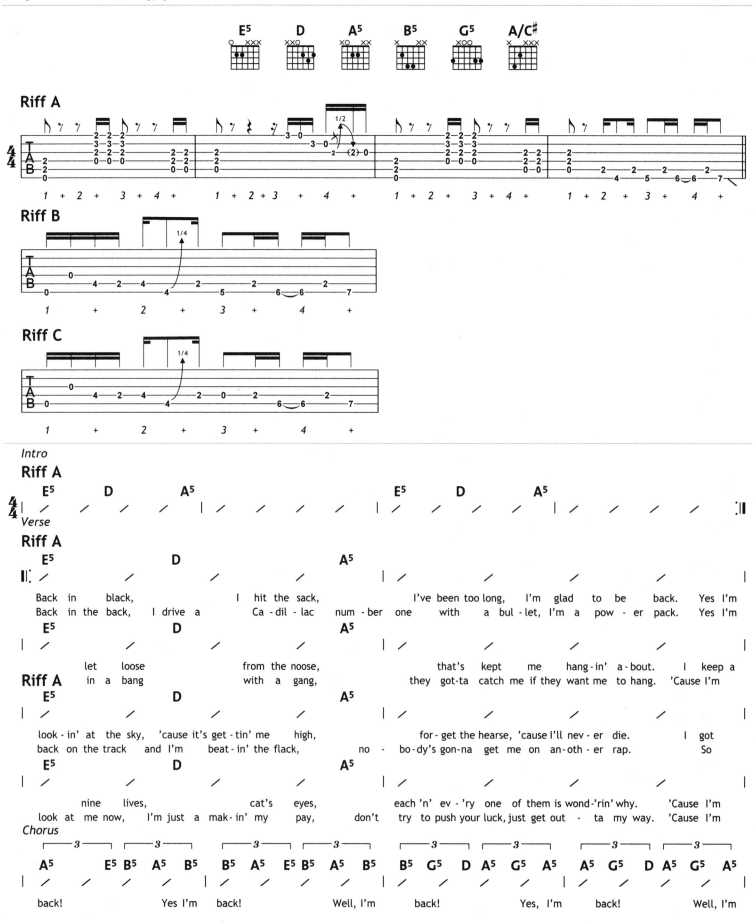

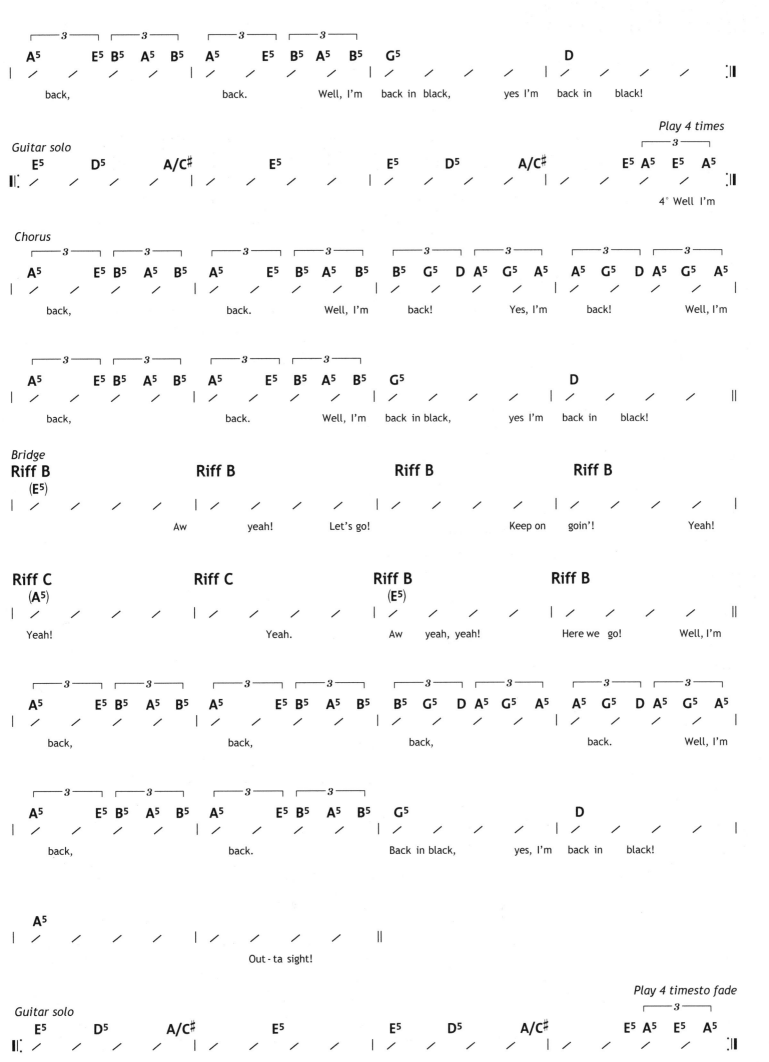

BLACK HOLE SUN

Words & Music by Chris Cornell

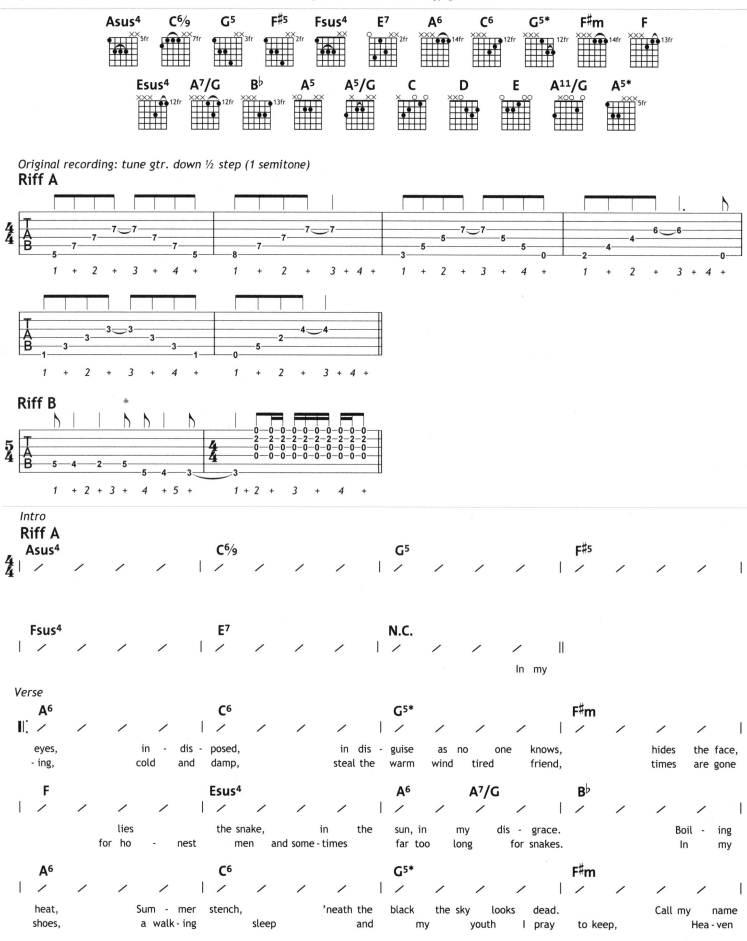

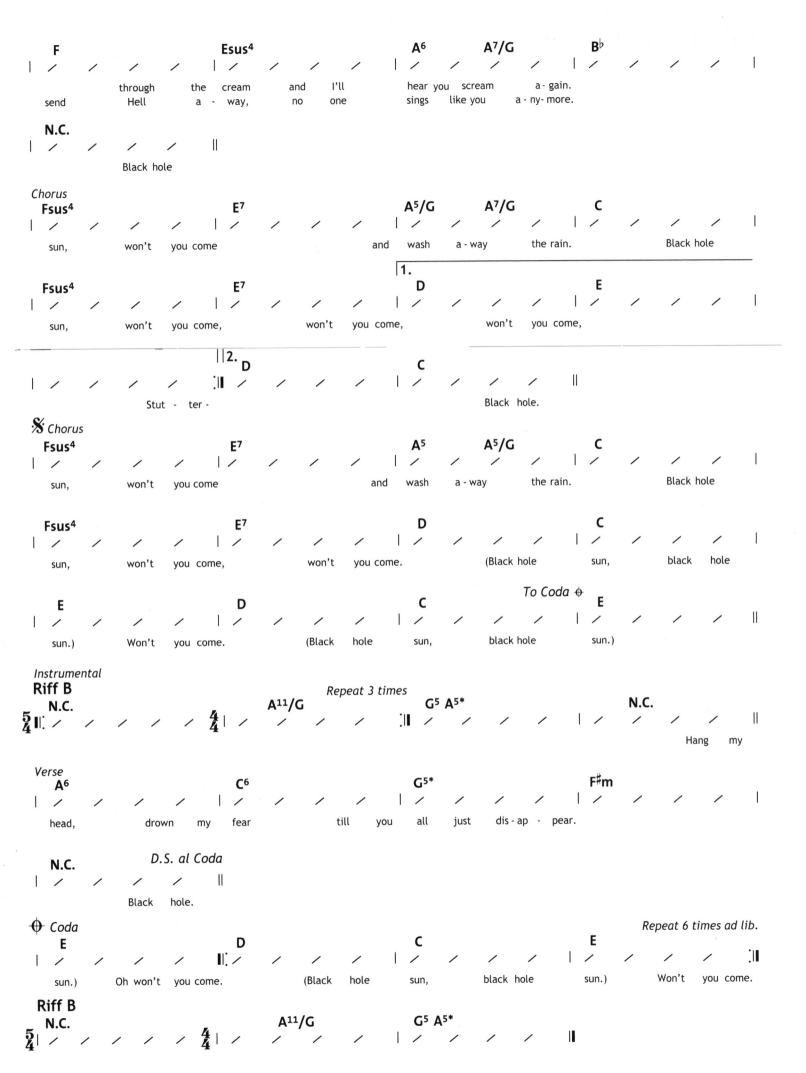

BORN TO BE WILD

Words & Music by Mars Bonfire

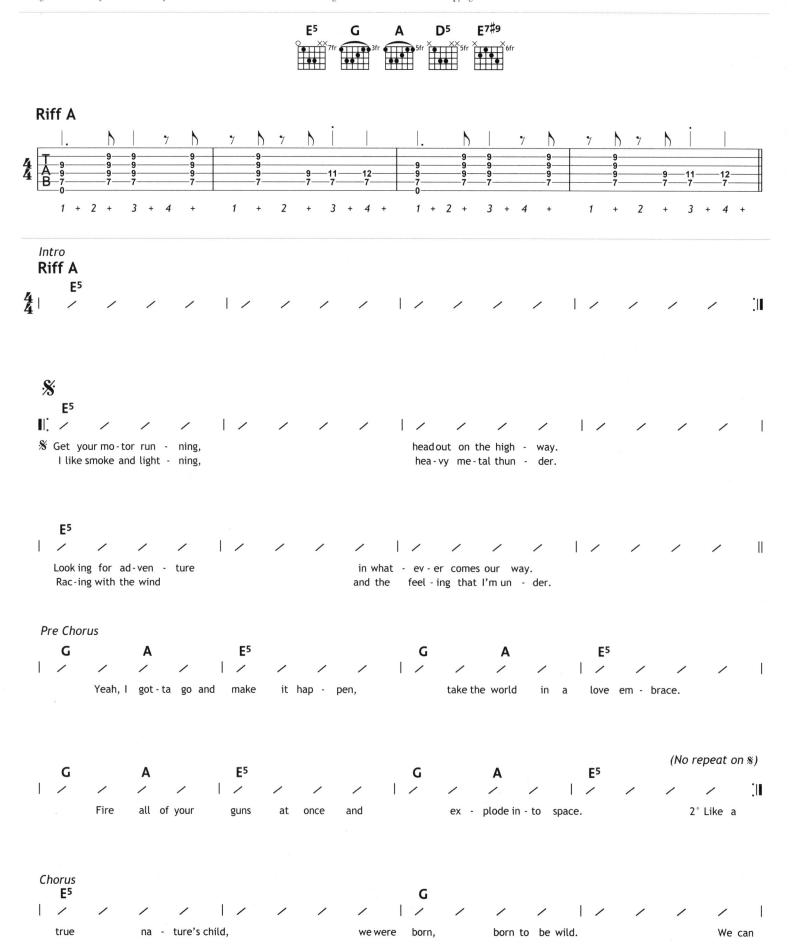

Riff A

Intro
Riff A

E⁵

℀

E⁵

Get your mo - tor run - ning, head out on the high - way.
I like smoke and light - ning, hea - vy me - tal thun - der.

E⁵

Look ing for ad - ven - ture in what - ev - er comes our way.
Rac - ing with the wind and the feel - ing that I'm un - der.

Pre Chorus

G   **A**   **E⁵**   **G**   **A**   **E⁵**

Yeah, I got - ta go and make it hap - pen, take the world in a love em - brace.

G   **A**   **E⁵**   **G**   **A**   **E⁵**

(No repeat on ℀)

Fire all of your guns at once and ex - plode in - to space. 2° Like a

Chorus

E⁵   **G**

true na - ture's child, we were born, born to be wild. We can

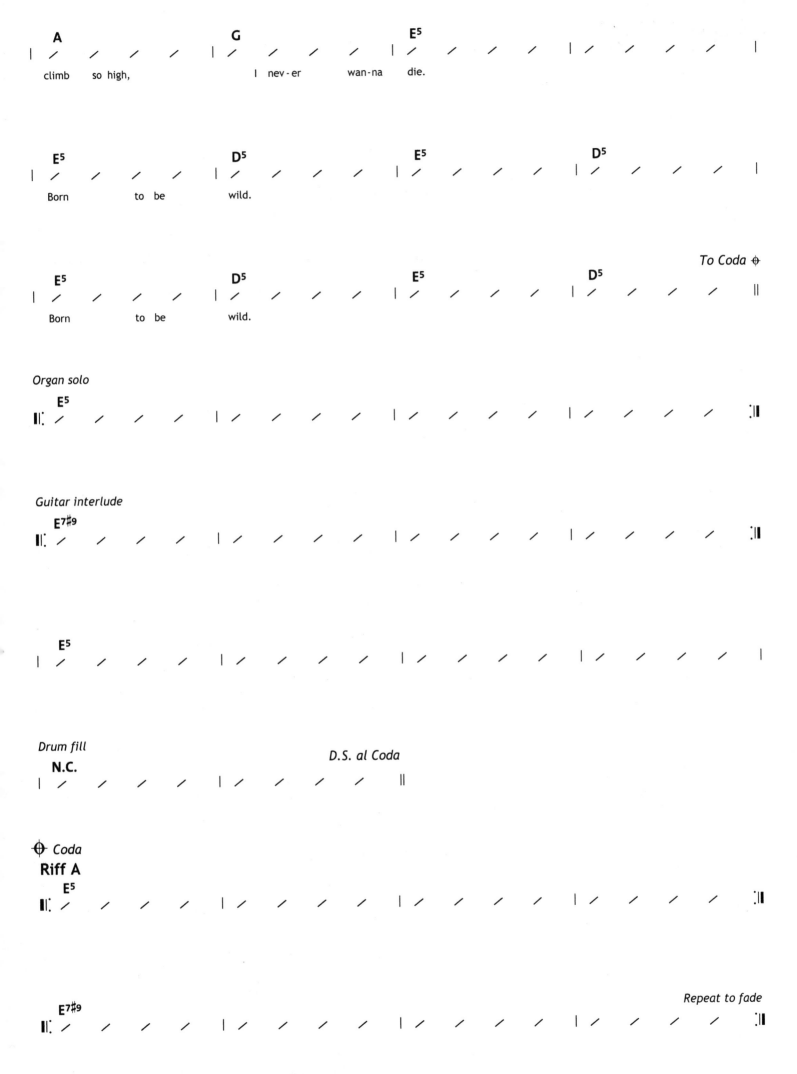

A   **G**   **E⁵**

climb   so high,   I nev-er   wan-na   die.

E⁵   **D⁵**   **E⁵**   **D⁵**

Born   to be   wild.

To Coda ⊕

E⁵   **D⁵**   **E⁵**   **D⁵**

Born   to be   wild.

Organ solo

E⁵

Guitar interlude

E⁷♯⁹

E⁵

Drum fill

N.C.

D.S. al Coda

⊕ *Coda*
Riff A

E⁵

Repeat to fade

E⁷♯⁹

CENTERFOLD

Words & Music by Seth Justman

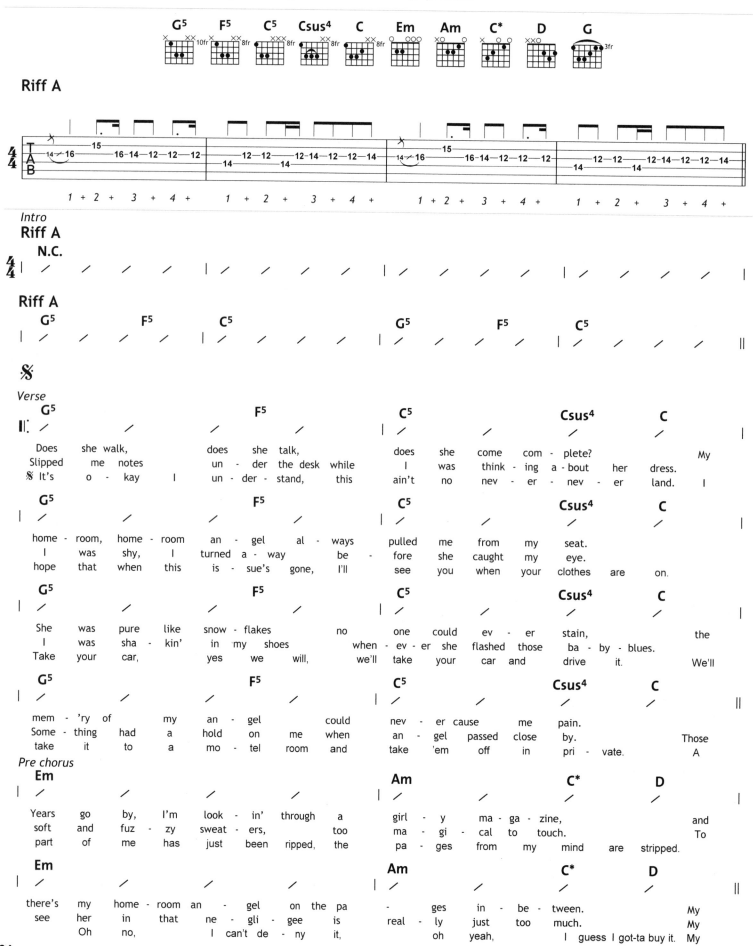

Chorus

| G⁵ | / | / | / | F⁵ | / | | C⁵ | / | / | / | / | |
blood   runs   cold,   my   me - mo - ry   has   just   been   sold,   my

| G⁵ | / | / | / | F⁵ | / | | C⁵ | / | / | / | / | |
an - gel   is   the   cen - tre - fold,   (an - gel   is   the   cen - tre - fold.)   My

| G⁵ | / | / | / | F⁵ | / | | C⁵ | / | / | / | / | |
blood   runs   cold,   my   me - mo - ry   has   just   been   sold.

To Coda ⊕

| G⁵ | / | / | / | F⁵ | / | | C⁵ | / | / | / | / | :‖
(An - gel   is   the   cen - tre - fold.)

Interlude

(Riff A *8vb*)

| G⁵ | / | / | / | F⁵ | / | | C⁵ | / | / | / | / | |
Na   na   na na   na   na,   na   na   na   na   na na na   na   na   na.

| G⁵ | / | / | / | F⁵ | / | | C⁵ | / | / | / | / | ‖
Na   na   na na   na   na,   na   na   na   na   na na na   na   na   na.

| G⁵ | / | / | / | F⁵ | / | | C⁵ | / | / | / | / | |
Na   na   na na   na   na,   na   na   na   na   na na na   na   na   na.

D.S. al Coda

| G⁵ | / | / | / | F⁵ | / | | C⁵ | / | / | / | / | ‖
Na   na   na na   na   na,   na   na   na   na   na na na   na   na.   Now lis - ten.

⊕ *Coda*

(Riff A *8vb*)

| G⁵ | / | / | / | F⁵ | / | | C | / | / | / | / | |
Na   na   na na   na   na,   na   na   na   na   na na na   na   na   na

| G | / | / | / | | N.C. | / | / | / | / | ‖
na.   *Alright,*   *alright.*   *One,*   *two,*   *three,*   *four.*

(Riff A *8vb*)

‖: | G⁵ | / | / | / | F⁵ | / | | C⁵ | / | / | / | / | |
Na   na   na na   na   na,   na   na   na   na   na na na   na   na.   Now lis - ten.

Repeat 5 times to fade

| G⁵ | / | / | / | F⁵ | / | | C⁵ | / | / | / | / | :‖
Na   na   na na   na   na,   na   na   na   na   na na na   na   na.   Now lis - ten.

CRAZY TRAIN

Words & Music by Ozzy Osbourne, Bob Daisley & Randy Rhoads

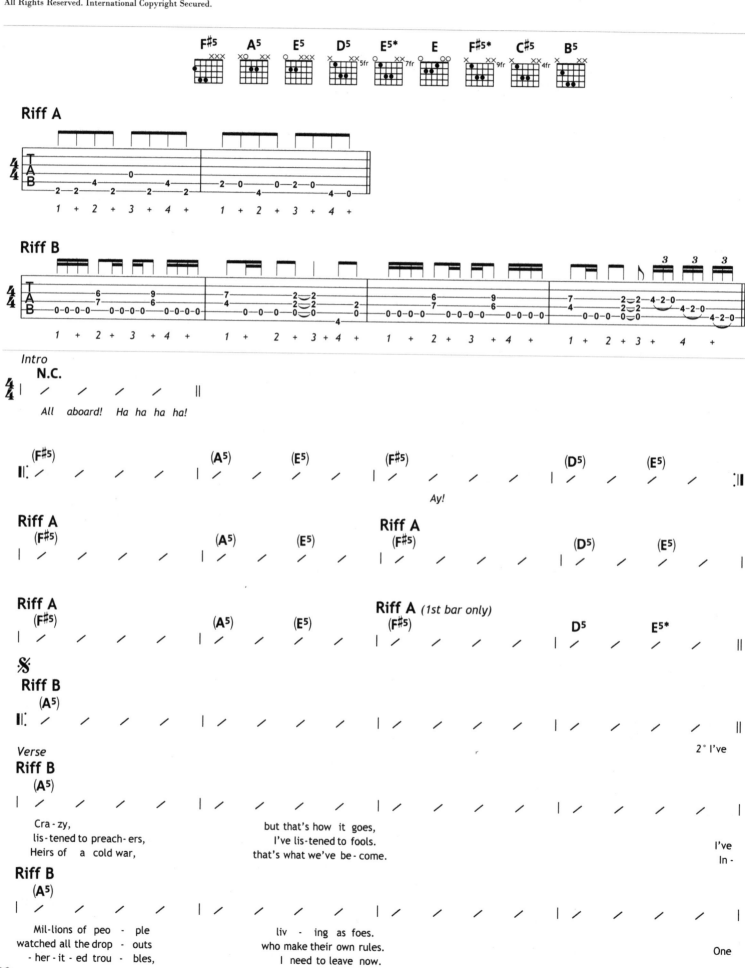

Riff B

(A5)

May-be
per-son con - di tioned
Cra - zy,

it's not too   late
for rule and con -trol,
I just can- not bear,

to
the
I'm

Riff B

(A5)

learn how to love
me - di - a sells   it
liv - ing with some-thing

and for-get how to hate.
and you lead the role.
that just is - n't fair.

Pre chorus

F#5   D5   F#5   D5

Men-tal wounds   not heal -   - ing,   life's a bit - ter shame.   I'm
Men-tal wounds   still scream - - ing,   driv-ing me   in - sane.   I'm
Men-tal wounds   not heal -   - ing,   who and what's   to blame?   I'm

Chorus

A5   E5   F#5

go - ing   off   the rails   on a cra - zy train.   I'm

A5   E5   F#5   A5   E5

go - ing   off   the rails   on a cra - zy train.

F#5   D5   E5   *To Coda* ⊕

Bridge

F#5   A5   E5   F#5   D5   E

I   know that things are go - ing wrong   for me,

F#5*   A5   E5   F#5*   D5   E

you got - ta lis - ten to my   words.   Yeah,

Guitar solo   *Play 3 times*

F#5*   E5* D5   C#5   B5   A5   F#5

(yeah.)

F#5*   E5* D5   C#5   B5   A5   E5

Interlude
Riff A   **Riff A**

(F#5)   (A5)   (E5)   (F#5)   (D5)   (E5)

Riff A   **Riff A** *(1st bar only)*   *D.S. al Coda*

(F#5)   (A5)   (E5)   (F#5)   D5   E5*

⊕ *Coda*   *Repeat to fade*
F#5   A5   E5   F#5   D5   E

CRAZY CRAZY NIGHTS

Words & Music by Paul Stanley & Adam Mitchell

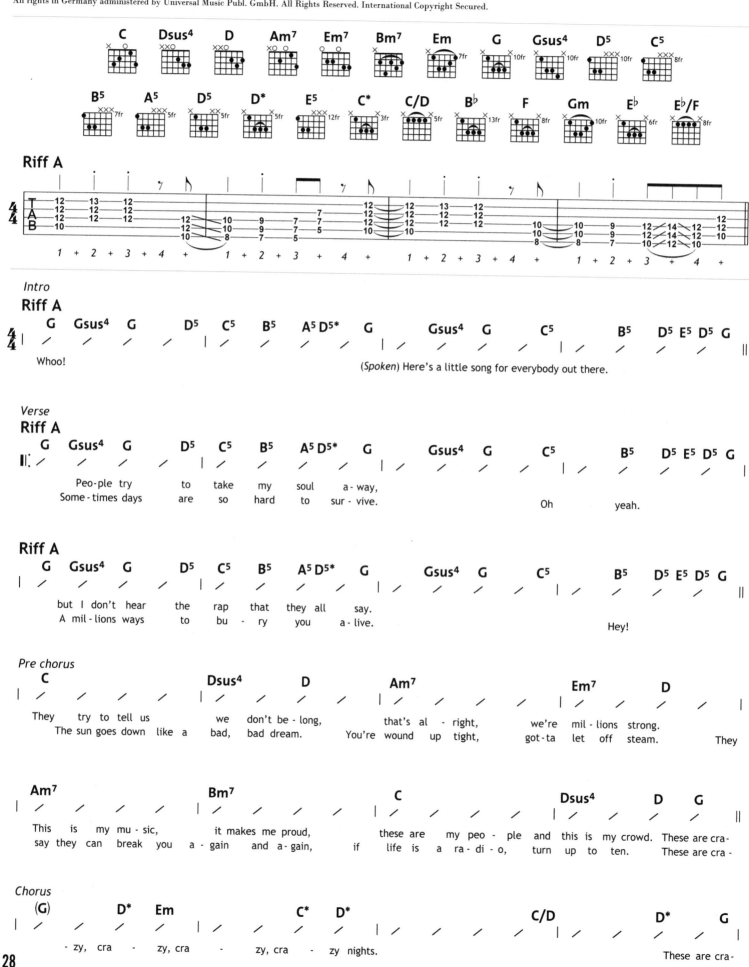

1.

(G)   D*   Em   C*   D*   C/D   D*   C*   G

| / / / / / | / / / / | / / / / | / / / / :||

\- zy, cra - zy, cra - zy, cra - zy nights.

2.

D*   B♭

| / / / / / ||

Well.   These are cra-

Chorus

B♭   F   Gm   E♭   F   E♭/F   F   B♭

| / / / / | / / / / | / / / / | / / / / |

\- zy, cra - zy, cra - zy, cra - zy nights.   Come on.   These are cra-

B♭   F   Gm   E♭   F   E♭/F   F   G

| / / / / | / / / / | / / / / | / / / / ||

\- zy, cra - zy, cra - zy, cra - zy nights.   Yeah.   Whoo!

Solo

(G)   D*   Em   C*   D   C/D   D*   G

| / / / / | / / / / | / / / / | / / / / |

(G)   D*   Em   C*   D   C/D   D*

| / / / / | / / / / | / / / / | / / / / ||

And

Pre chorus

C   Dsus⁴   D   Am⁷   Em⁷   D*

| / / / / | / / / / | / / / / | / / / / |

they try   to tell us   that we don't be - long. But that's al - right, we're mil - lions strong.

Am⁷   Bm⁷   C   Dsus⁴   D

| / / / / | / / / / | / / / / | / / / / |

You are my peo - ple,   you are my crowd,   this is our mu - sic,   we love it loud.

D   C*

| / / / / ||

Bridge
Riff A

| G | Gsus⁴ | G | D⁵ | C⁵ | B⁵ | A⁵ D⁵* | G | Gsus⁴ | G | C⁵ | B⁵ | D⁵ E⁵ D⁵ G |

| ⌿ | ⌿ | ⌿ | ⌿ | ⌿ | ⌿ | ⌿ | ⌿ | ⌿ | ⌿ | ⌿ | ⌿ | ⌿ |

Yeah,   (*Spoken*) and nobody's gonna change me.

Riff A (*1st 2 bars*)

| G | Gsus⁴ | G | D⁵ | C⁵ | B⁵ | A⁵ D⁵* | G |

'cause that's who I am.   Ooh!   These are cra-

Chorus

| (G) | D* | Em | C* | D | C/D | D* | G |

- zy, cra - zy, cra - zy, cra - zy nights.   These are cra-

| (G) | D* | Em | C* | D | C/D | **1.** D* | C* | G |

- zy, cra - zy, cra - zy, cra - zy nights.   These are cra-

2.

| D* | B♭ |

These are cra-

Chorus

| (B♭) | F | Gm | E♭ | F | E♭/F | F | B♭ |

- zy, cra - zy, cra - zy, cra - zy nights.   Oh   yeah.   These are cra

Repeat to fade

| (B♭) | F | Gm | E♭ | F | E♭/F | F | B♭ |

- zy, cra - zy, cra - zy, cra - zy nights.   Come on!   These are cra-

(DON'T FEAR) THE REAPER

Words & Music by Donald Roeser

Riff A

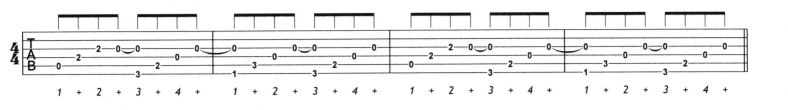

Riff A

Verse
Riff A

All   our times   have   come,

Riff A

here   but now   they're   gone.

Pre chorus

Sea - sons don't fear the reap - er,   nor do the wind,   the sun or the rain.

(We can be like   they

Come on ba -

are.)

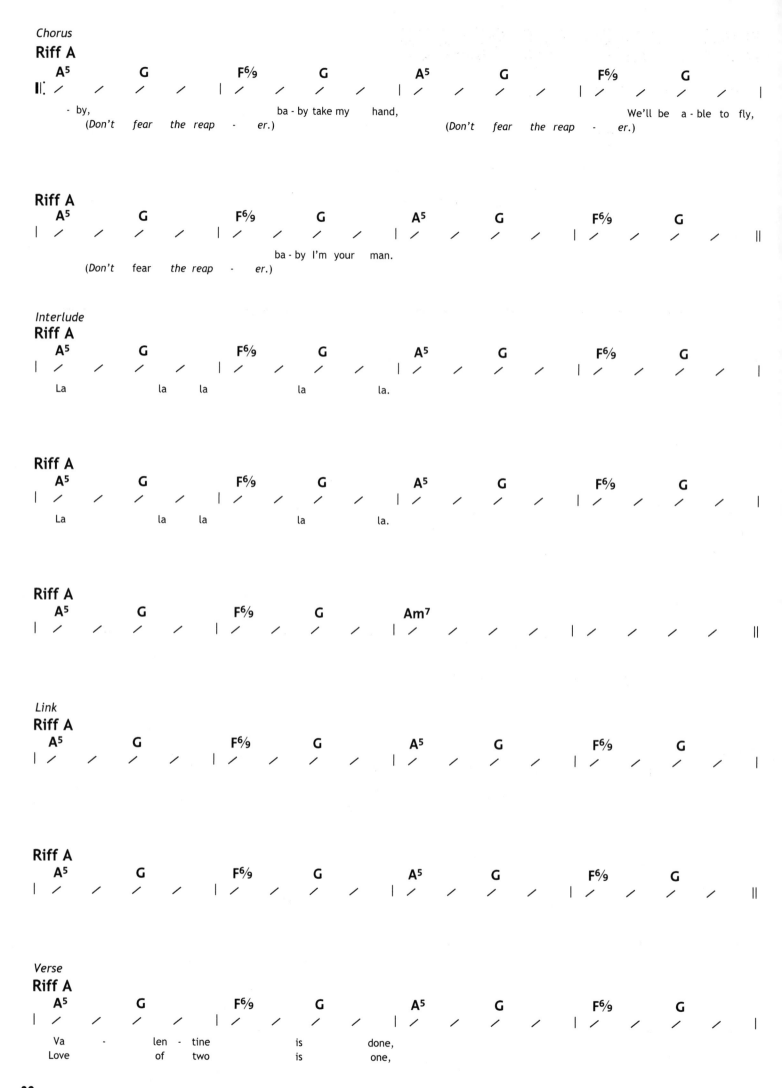

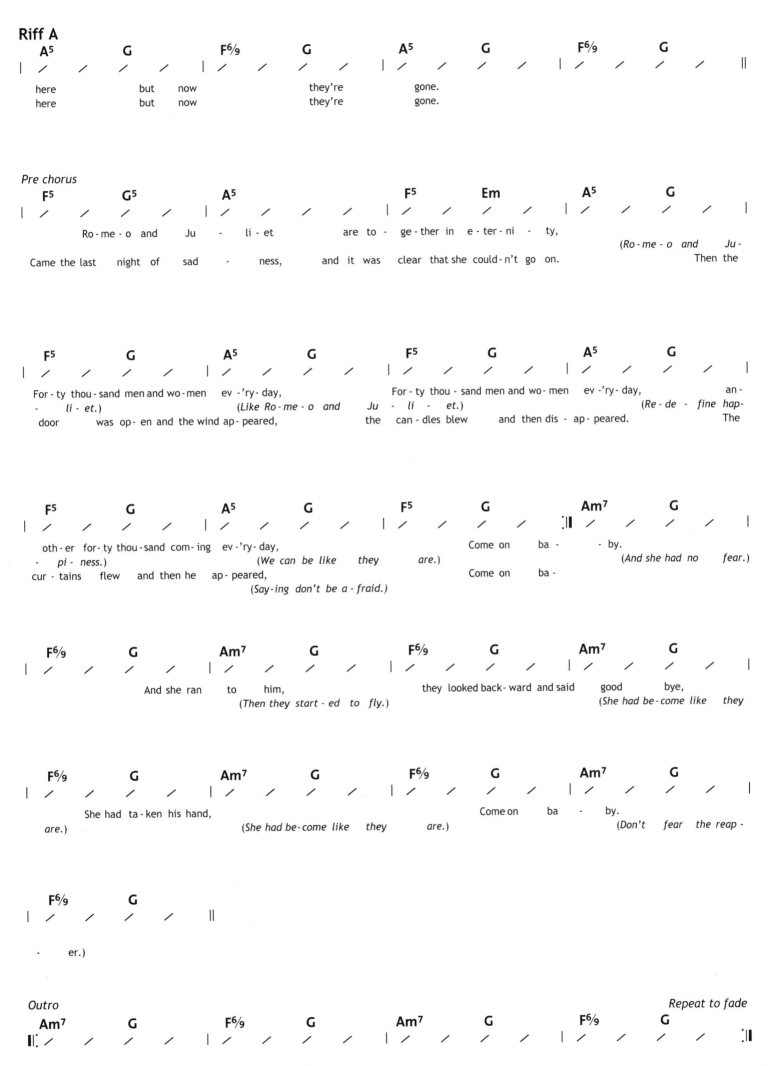

EYE OF THE TIGER

Words & Music by Frank Sullivan III & Jim Peterik

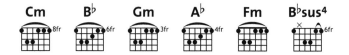

Riff A

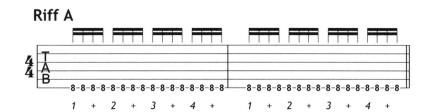

Riff B

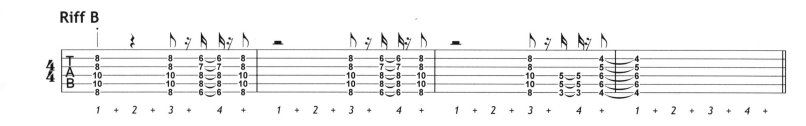

Intro

Riff A

Riff B

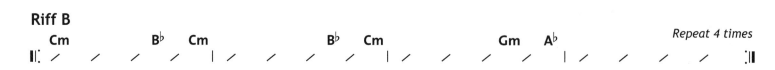

Riff A

Verse

Ri - sin' up,   back on the street,   did my time,   took my chan - ces.

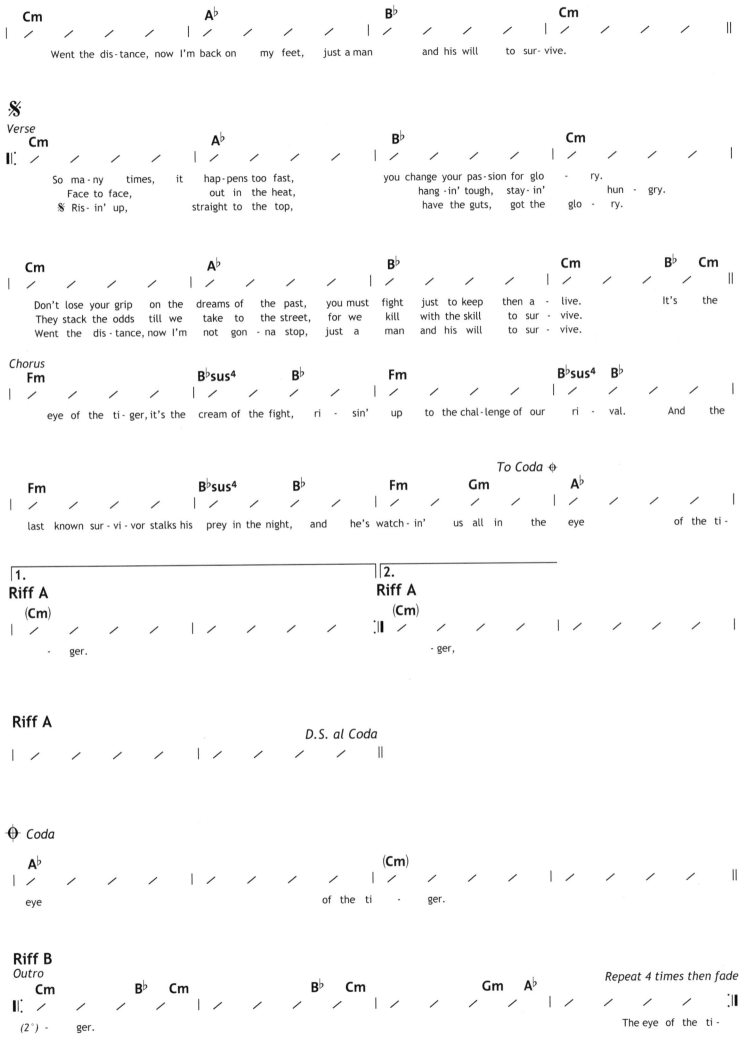

ENTER SANDMAN

Words & Music by James Hetfield, Lars Ulrich & Kirk Hammett

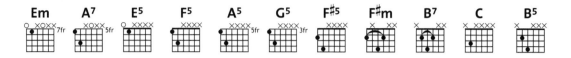

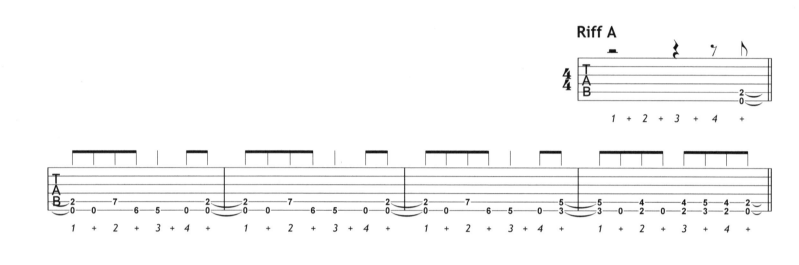

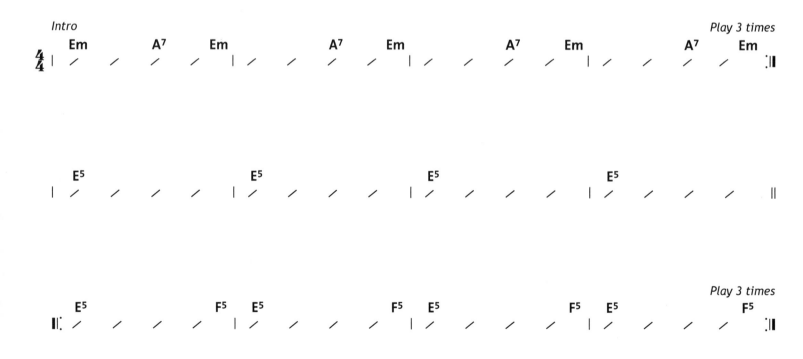

Verse

E5   F5   E5   F5   E5   G5   E5 F#5 E5 F#5 G5 F#5 E5

Say your prayers, lit-tle one, don't for-get, my son, to in-clude ev-ery-one.
Some-thing's wrong, shut he light, hea-vy thoughts to-night and they aren't of Snow White.

E5   F5   E5   F5   E5   G5   E5 F#5 E5 F#5 G5 F#5 E5

I tuck you in, warm with-in, keep you free from sin till the sand-man he comes.
Dreams of war, dreams of liars, dreams of dra-gon's fire and of things that will bite.

Pre Chorus

F#m   B7   F#m   B7   F#m   B7   F#m   B7   F#5

Sleep with one eye op-en, grip-ping your pil-low tight. Ex-

Chorus

F#5   C B5   F#5   C B5   F#5   C B5   E5   F#5

- - it: light, en - - ter: night. Take

C B5   E5   E5 F#5 E5 F#5 G5 F#5 (E5)

my hand, we're off to nev-er-nev-er land.

Riff A

E5   A5   E5   A5   E5   A5   G5   E5 F#5 E5 F#5 G5 F#5 E5

E5   A5   E5   A5   E5   A5   G5   E5 F#5 E5 F#5 G5 F#5 E5

|1.|

|2.|

E5

Solo

Riff A

E5   A5   E5   A5   E5   A5   G5   E5 F#5 E5 F#5 G5 F#5 E5

F#m   B7   F#m   B7   F#m   B7   F#m   B7   F#m

F#5   C B5   F#5   C B5   F#5   C B5   E5   F#5

C B5   E5   *Gtr. fill*   E5

E5   E5   E5

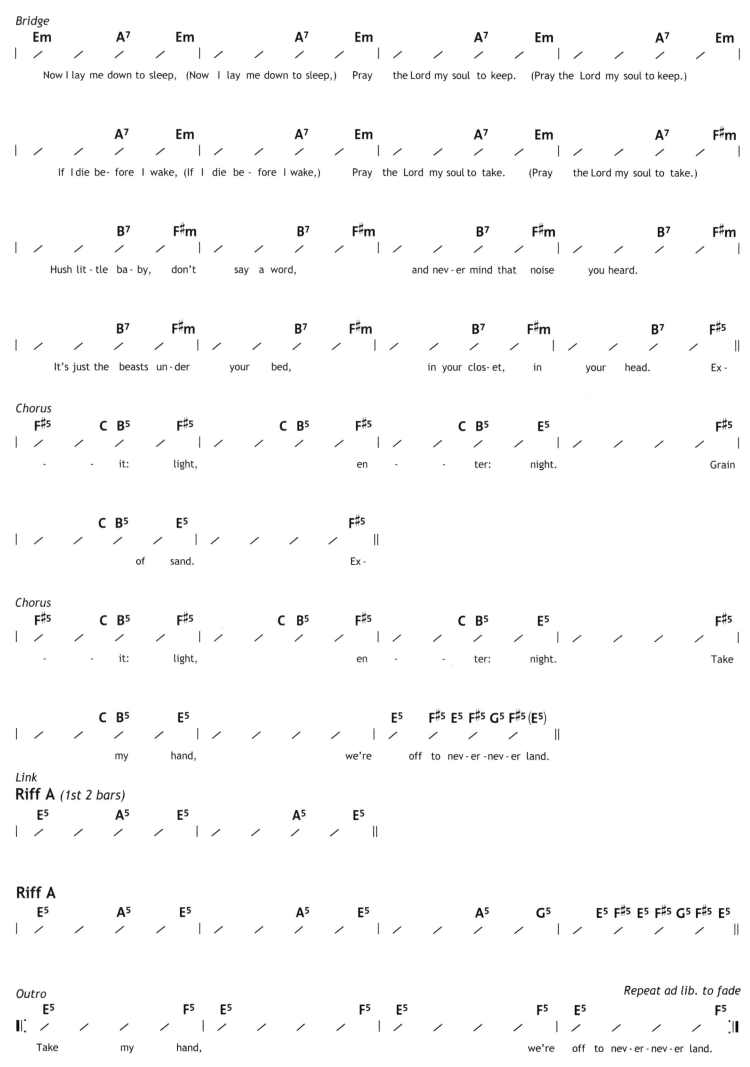

FEAR OF THE DARK

Words & Music by Steve Harris

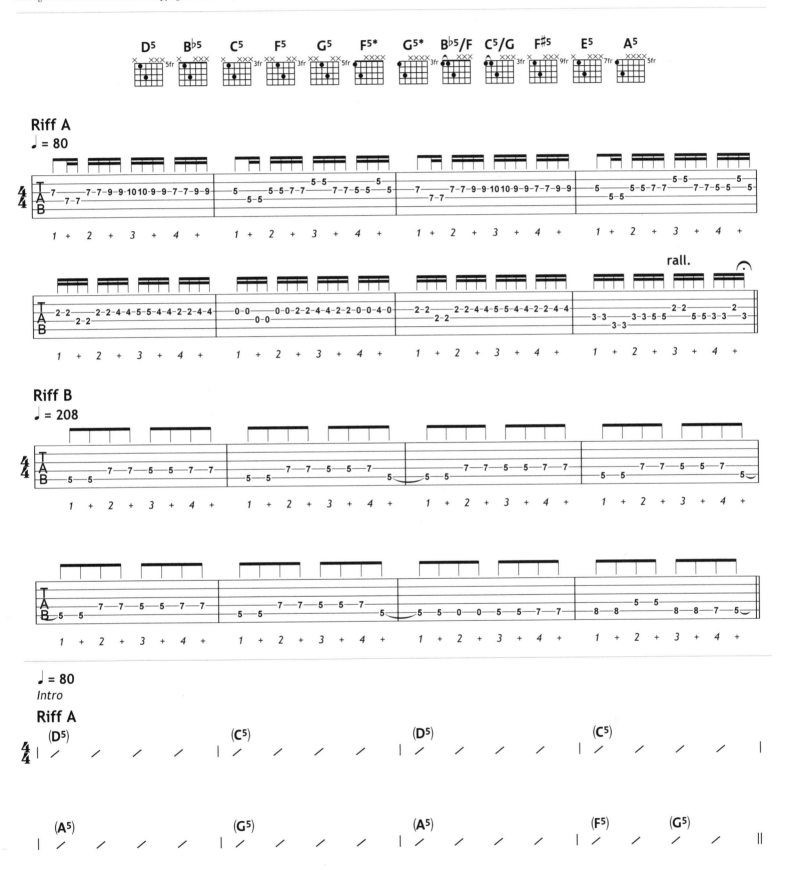

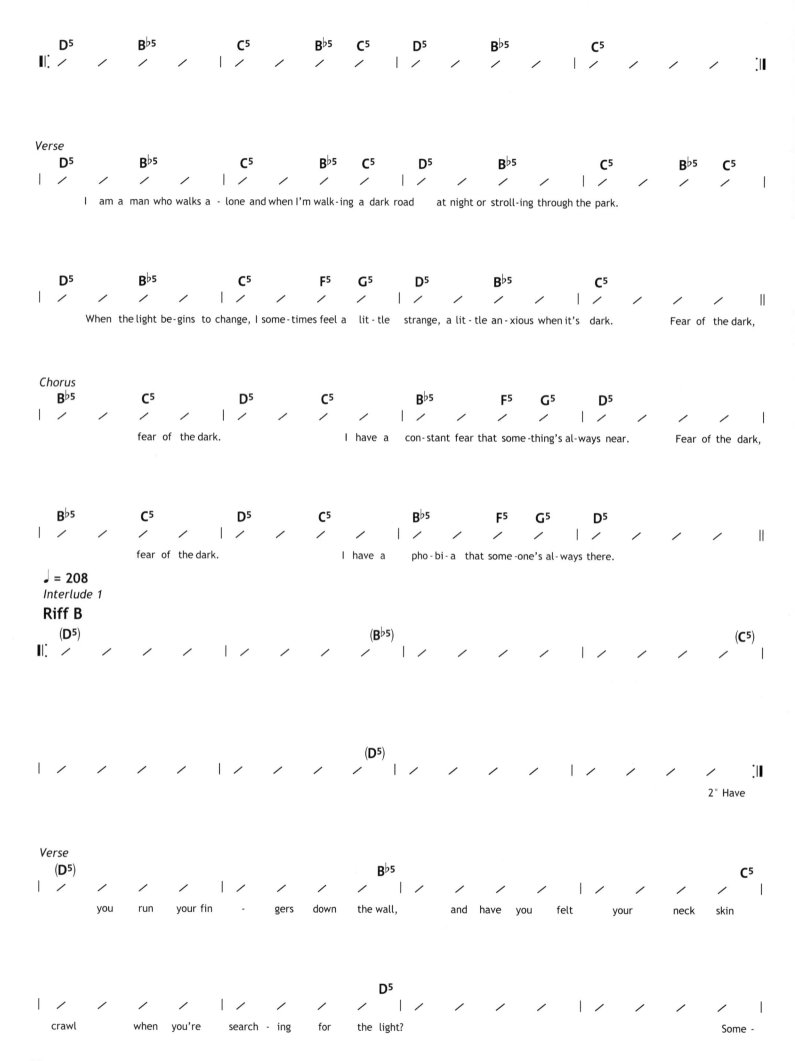

Verse

I am a man who walks a - lone and when I'm walk-ing a dark road   at night or stroll-ing through the park.

When the light be-gins to change, I some-times feel a lit-tle strange, a lit-tle an-xious when it's dark.   Fear of the dark,

Chorus

fear of the dark.   I have a con-stant fear that some-thing's al-ways near.   Fear of the dark,

fear of the dark.   I have a pho-bi-a that some-one's al-ways there.

♩ = 208
Interlude 1
Riff B

2° Have

Verse

you   run   your fin - gers   down   the wall,   and have you   felt   your   neck   skin

crawl   when   you're   search - ing   for   the light?   Some -

40

B♭5   C5

- times when you're scared to take a look   at the cor - ner of the room,

D5   B♭5

you've sensed that some - thing's watch - ing you.   Fear of the dark,

Chorus
(B♭5)   C5   D5   C5   B♭5

fear of the dark.   I have a con-
fear of the dark.   I have a pho-

F5*   G5*   D5   B♭5

- stant fear that some - thing's al - ways near.   Fear of the dark,
- bi - a that some - one's al - ways there.   Have

Verse
(D5)   B♭5   C5   F5*   G5*   D5

you ev - er been a - lone at night,   thought you heard foot - steps be - hind
ing hor - ror films the night be - fore   de - ba - ting witch - es and folk - lore,

B♭5   C5   D5

and turned a - round and no one's there?
the un - kown trou - bles on your mind.

B♭5   C5   F5*   G5*   D5

And as you quick - en up your pace,   you find it hard to look a - gain
May - be your mind is play - ing tricks,   you sense and sud - den - ly eyes fix

To Coda
B♭5   C5   B♭5

be - cause you're sure there's some - one there.   Fear of the dark,
on dan - cing sha - dows from be - hind.   Fear of the dark,

Half time feel
Chorus
(B♭5)   C5   D5   C5

fear of the dark.   I have a con-
fear of the dark.   I have a pho-

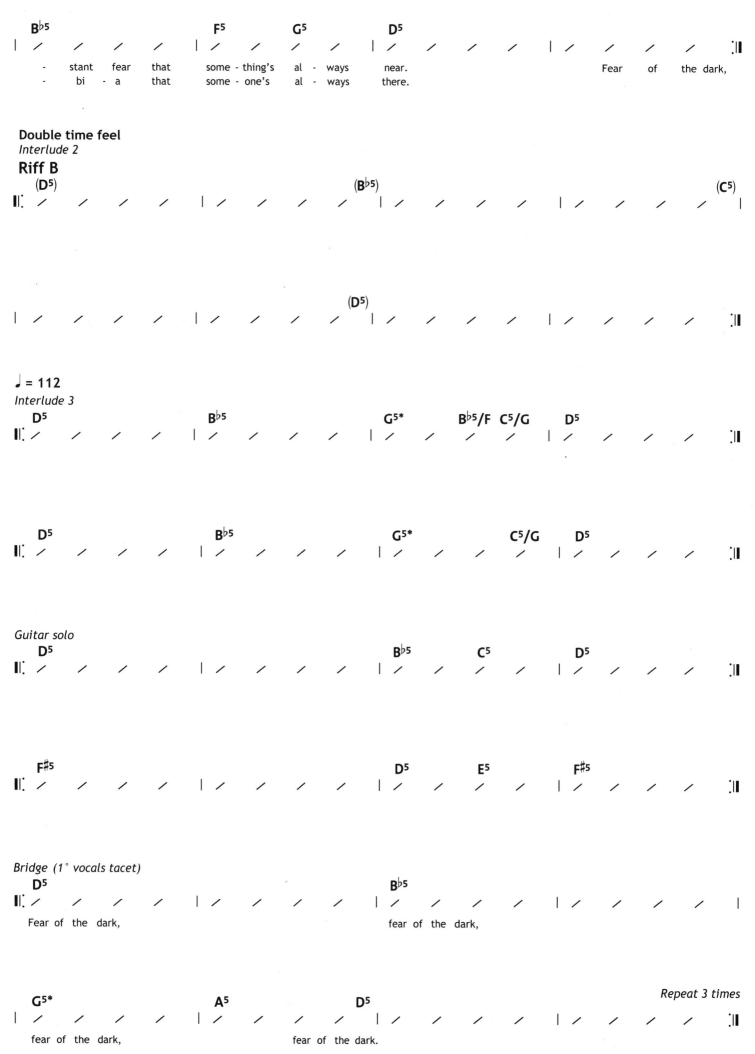

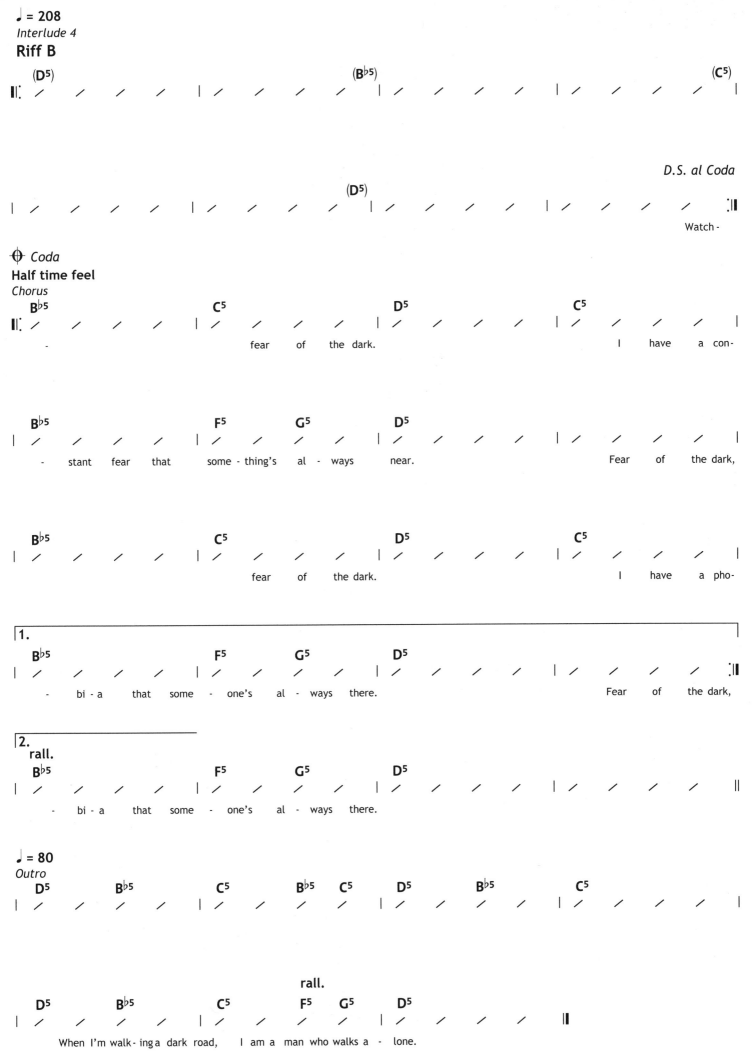

GIMME ALL YOUR LOVIN'

Words & Music by Billy Gibbons, Dusty Hill & Frank Beard

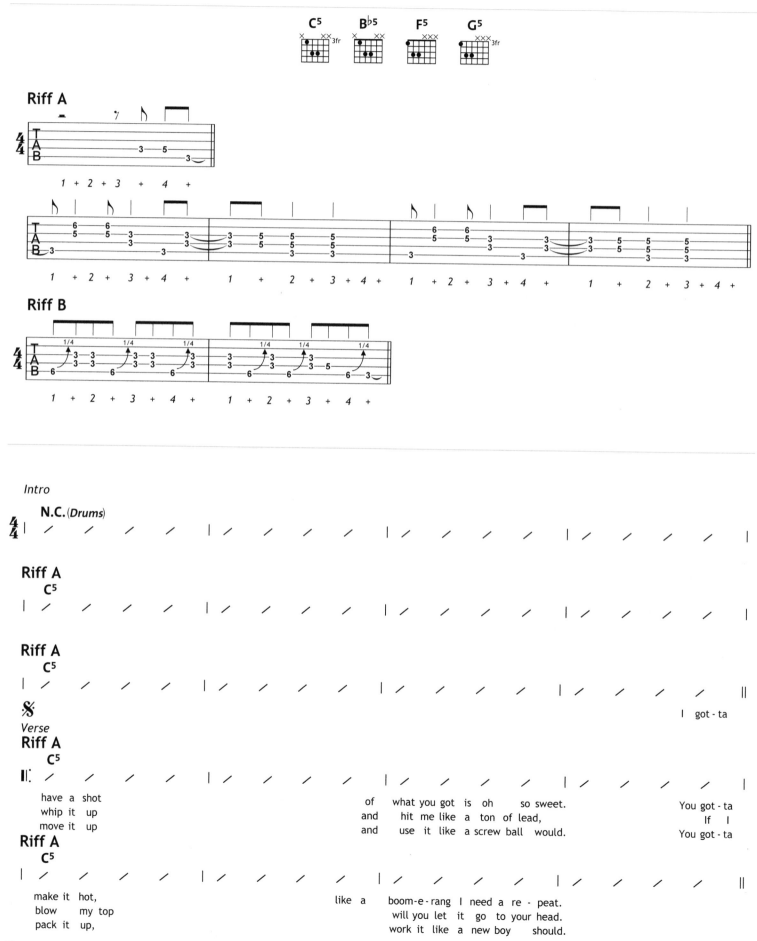

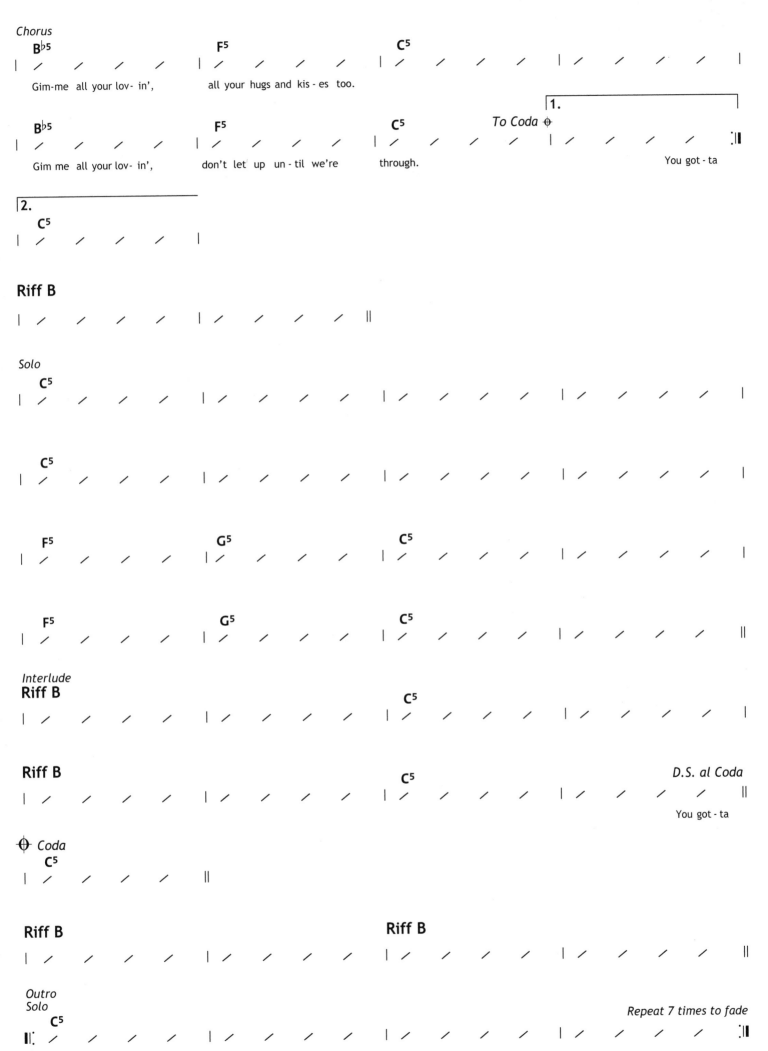

Chorus

B♭5   **F5**   **C5**

Gim-me all your lov- in',   all your hugs and kis - es too.

1.

B♭5   **F5**   **C5**   *To Coda* ⊕

Gim me all your lov- in',   don't let up un - til we're   through.   You got - ta

2.

C5

Riff B

Solo

C5

C5

F5   **G5**   **C5**

F5   **G5**   **C5**

Interlude
Riff B   **C5**

Riff B   *D.S. al Coda*

C5

You got - ta

⊕ *Coda*
C5

Riff B   **Riff B**

Outro
Solo
C5   *Repeat 7 times to fade*

HARD TO HANDLE

Words & Music by Otis Redding, Alvertis Isbell & Allen Jones

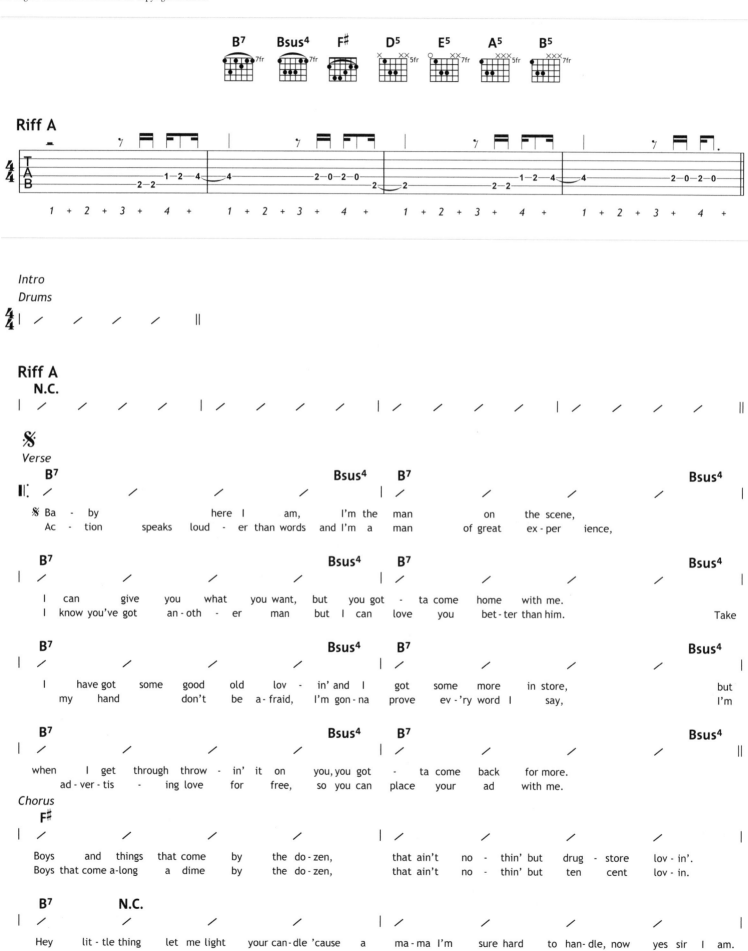

1.

D5   E5   A5 E5   B5

| / / / / | / / / / :||

To Coda ⊕
D.S. al Coda

2, 3.

A5 E5 B5   A5 E5 B5   A5 E5 B5   A5 E5   B5

| / / / / | / / / / | / / / / | / / / / ||

Yeah,   hard   to han - dle now,   oh ba - by.

⊕ *Coda*

Solo

B7   Bsus4 B7   Bsus4 B7   Bsus4 B7   Bsus4

| / / / / | / / / / | / / / / | / / / / |

B7   Bsus4 B7   Bsus4 B7   Bsus4 B7   Bsus4

| / / / / | / / / / | / / / / | / / / / ||

Chorus

F#7

| / / / / | / / / / | / / / / |

Boys that come a-long   a dime   by   the do - zen,   that ain't no - thin' but   ten   cent   lov - in.

B7   N.C.

| / / / / | / / / / | / / / / |

Hey   lit - tle thing   let me light   your can-dle 'cause a   ma - ma I'm   sure hard   to han dle, now   yes sir I am.

Solo

A5 E5 B5   A5 E5 B5   A5 E5 B5   A5 E5 B5

| / / / / | / / / / | / / / / | / / / / ||

Yeah,   so hard to   han-dle now,   oh yeah.

B7   Bsus4 B7   Bsus4 B7   Bsus4 B7   Bsus4

| / / / / | / / / / | / / / / | / / / / |

Ba - by,   well good   lov - in',   ba - by,   ba - by, ow,   good

B7   Bsus4 B7   Bsus4 B7   Bsus4 B7   Bsus4

| / / / / | / / / / | / / / / | / / / / ||

lov - in'.   You need good   lov - in'.   I got to   have it,   oh yeah.

A5 E5 B5   A5 E5 B5   A5 E5 B5   A5 E5 B5

| / / / / | / / / / | / / / / | / / / / ||

47

GET THE FUNK OUT

Words & Music by Nuno Bettencourt & Gary Cherone

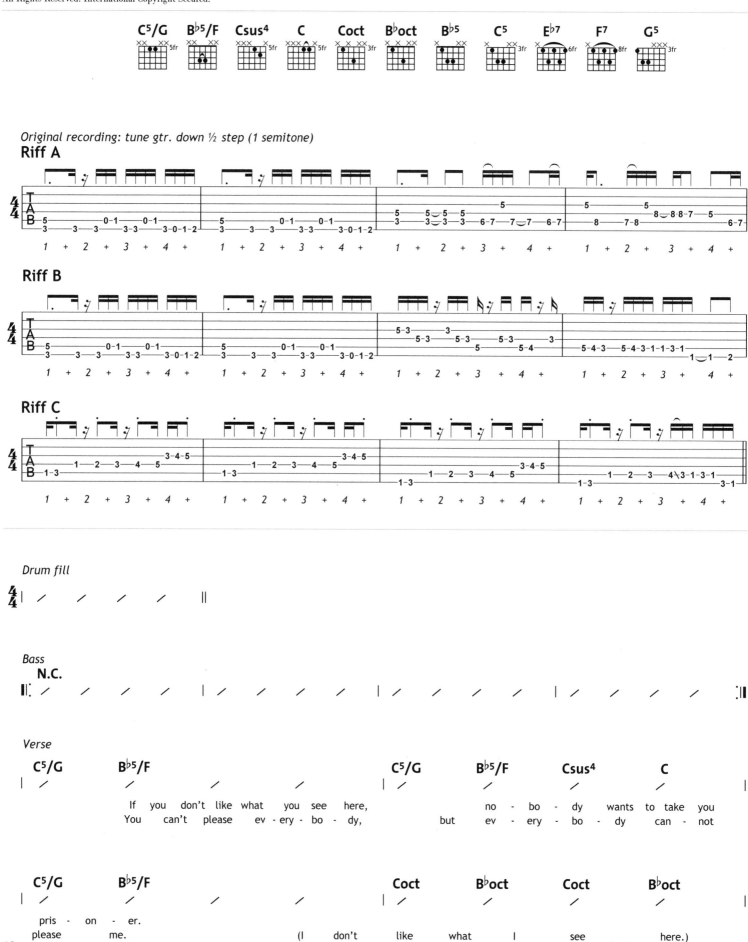

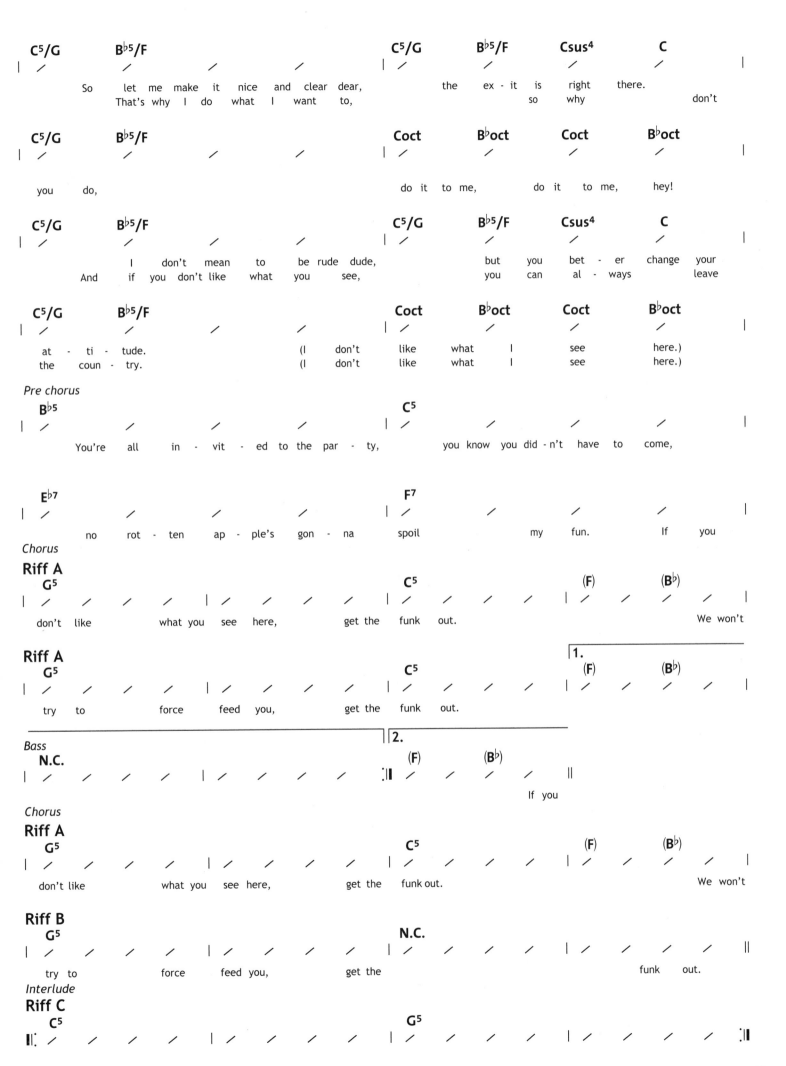

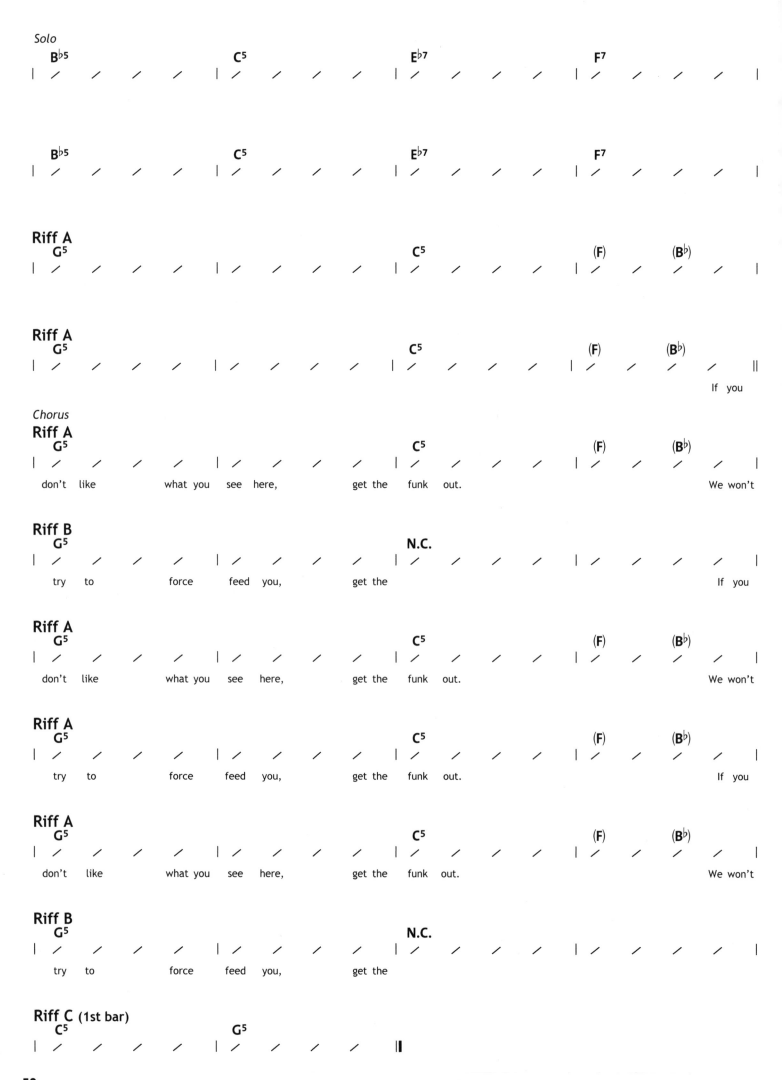

HELTER SKELTER

Words & Music by John Lennon & Paul McCartney

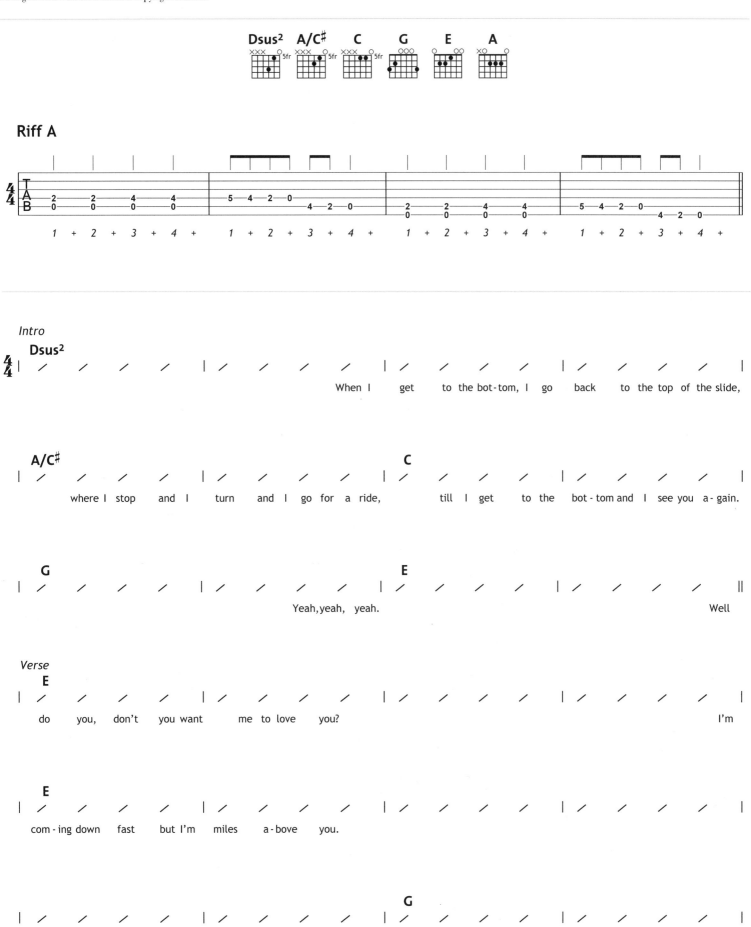

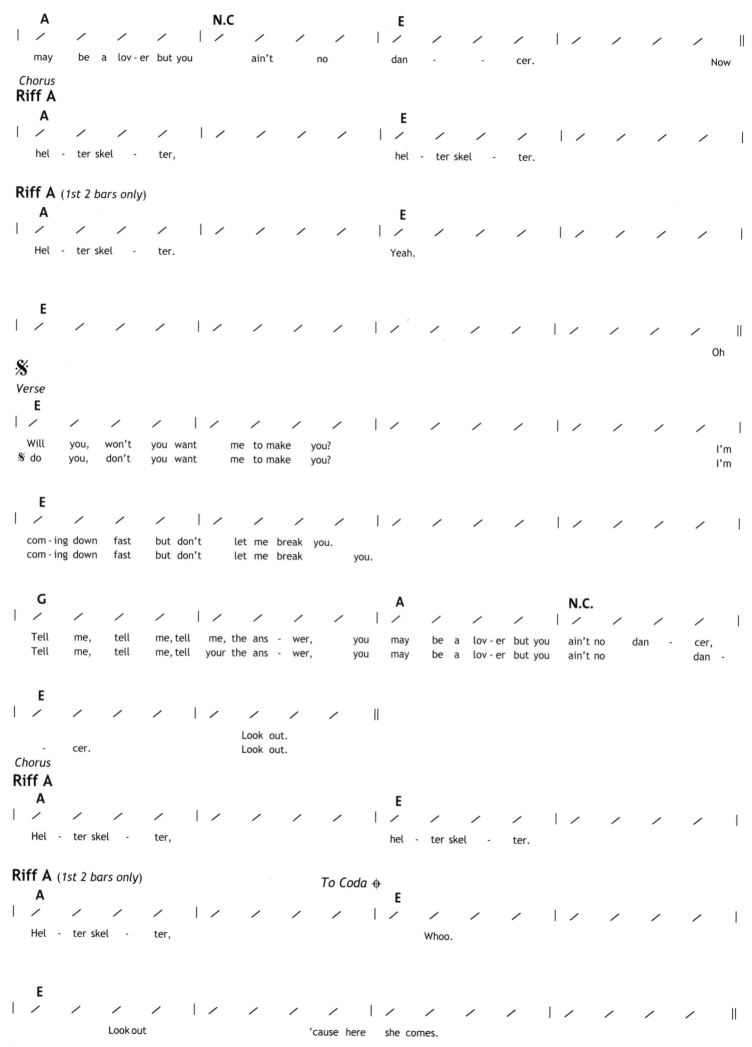

A   N.C   E

may   be   a   lov - er   but you   ain't   no   dan - - cer.   Now

Chorus

Riff A

A   E

hel - ter skel - ter,   hel - ter skel - ter.

Riff A *(1st 2 bars only)*

A   E

Hel - ter skel - ter.   Yeah.

E

                                           Oh

𝄋

Verse

E

Will   you,   won't   you want   me to make   you?   I'm
𝄋 do   you,   don't   you want   me to make   you?   I'm

E

com - ing down   fast   but don't   let me break   you.
com - ing down   fast   but don't   let me break   you.

G   A   N.C.

Tell   me,   tell   me, tell   me, the ans - wer,   you   may   be   a   lov - er   but you   ain't no   dan - cer,
Tell   me,   tell   me, tell   your the ans - wer,   you   may   be   a   lov - er   but you   ain't no   dan -

E

                     Look out.
- cer.   Look out.

Chorus

Riff A

A   E

Hel - ter skel - ter,   hel - ter skel - ter.

Riff A *(1st 2 bars only)*

                   To Coda ⊕

A   E

Hel - ter skel - ter,   Whoo.

E

     Look out   'cause here   she comes.

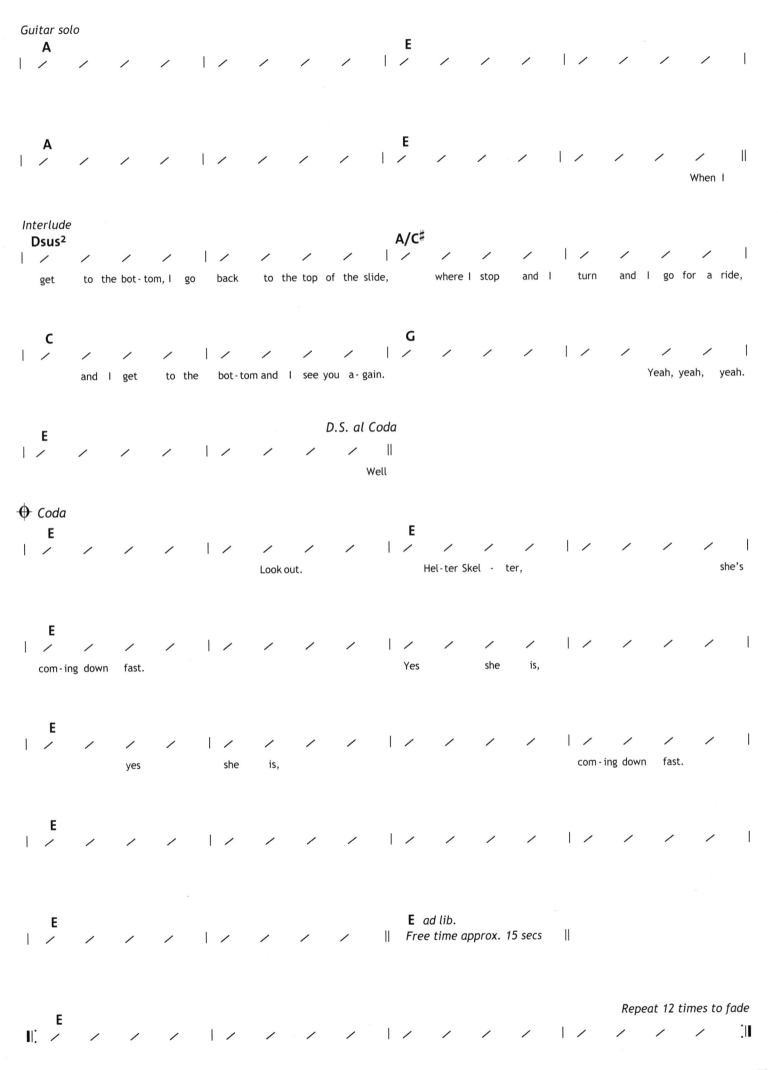

HERE I GO AGAIN

Words & Music by David Coverdale & Bernie Marsden

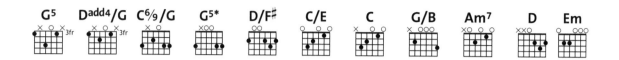

Riff A

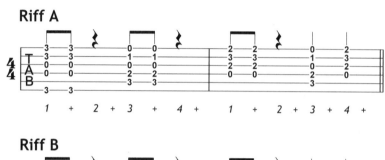

Riff B

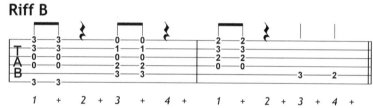

Intro

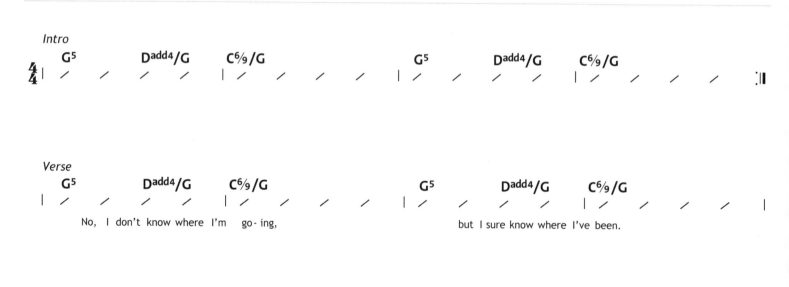

Verse

No, I don't know where I'm go-ing,   but I sure know where I've been.

Hang-ing on the pro-mis-es in songs of yes-ter-day.   And I've make up my mind,

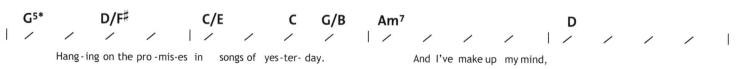

I ain't wast-ing no more time.

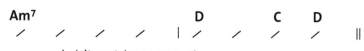

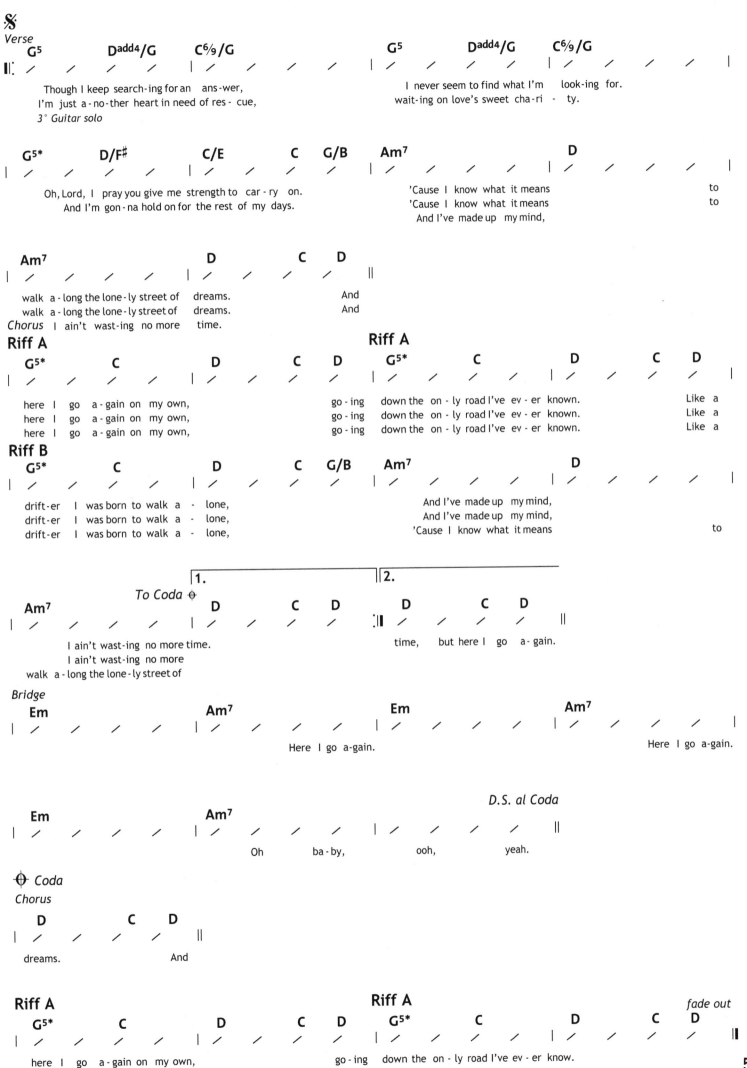

HOLD THE LINE

Words & Music by David Paich

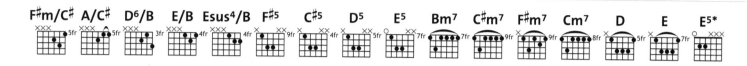

Riff A

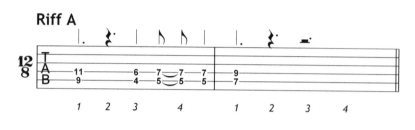

Riff B

Intro

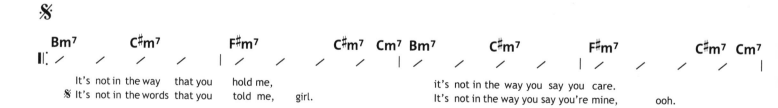

It's not in the way   that you   hold me,   it's not in the way you say you care.

It's not in the words that you   told me,   girl.   It's not in the way you say you're mine,   ooh.

It's not in the way you've been   treat-ing my friends.   It's not in the way that   you   stayed   till the end.

It's not in the way that you   came   back to me.   It's not in the way that your love set me free.

Bm⁷ / **C♯m⁷** / | **D** / **E** / ||

It's not in the way you look or the things that you say that you'll do. Hold the

Chorus
Riff A
F♯5 / / **C♯5** **D5** / | / / / | **Riff A** **F♯5** / / **C♯5** **D5** / **E5** / | / / / |

line,   love isn't al-ways   on   time,   oh,   oh,   oh.   Hold the

Riff A
F♯5 / / **C♯5** **D5** / **E5** / | / / / |

To Coda ⊕
Riff B (2° Riff A)
F♯5 / / **C♯5** **D5** / **E5** / | / / **E** **C♯m⁷ Cm⁷** :||

line,   love isn't al-ways   on   time,   oh,   oh,   oh.

Guitar solo
                                                    Repeat 4 times
Riff A   **Riff A (4° Riff B)**   *4° D.S. al Coda*
F♯5 / / **C♯5** **D5** / **E5** / | ||: / / / | **F♯5** / / **C♯5** **D5** / **E5** / | / / / :||

⊕ *Coda*
Riff A
F♯5 / / **C♯5** **D5** / **E5** / | / / / ||

time,   love isn't al-ways   on   time.   Hold the

Chorus
Riff A
F♯5 / / **C♯5** **D5** / **E5** / | **Riff A** **F♯5** / / **C♯5** **D5** / **E5** / | / / / |

line,   love isn't al-ways   on   time,   love isn't al-ways   love   isn't al-ways on   time. Hold the

Riff A
F♯5 / / **C♯5** **D5** / **E5** / | **Riff A** **F♯5** / / **C♯5** **D5** / **E5** / | / / / |

line,   love isn't al-ways   on   time,   love isn't al-ways   on

Riff A
F♯5 / / **C♯5** **D5** / **E5** / | **Riff A** **F♯5** / / **C♯5** **D5** / **E5** / | / / / |

time,   love isn't al-ways   on   time,   love isn't al-ways   on

Riff A
F♯5 / / **C♯5** **D5** / **E5*** / | / / / ||

time,   oh,   oh,   oh.

JUST BECAUSE

Words & Music by Perry Farrell, Dave Navarro, Chris Chaney, Stephen Perkins & Bob Ezrin

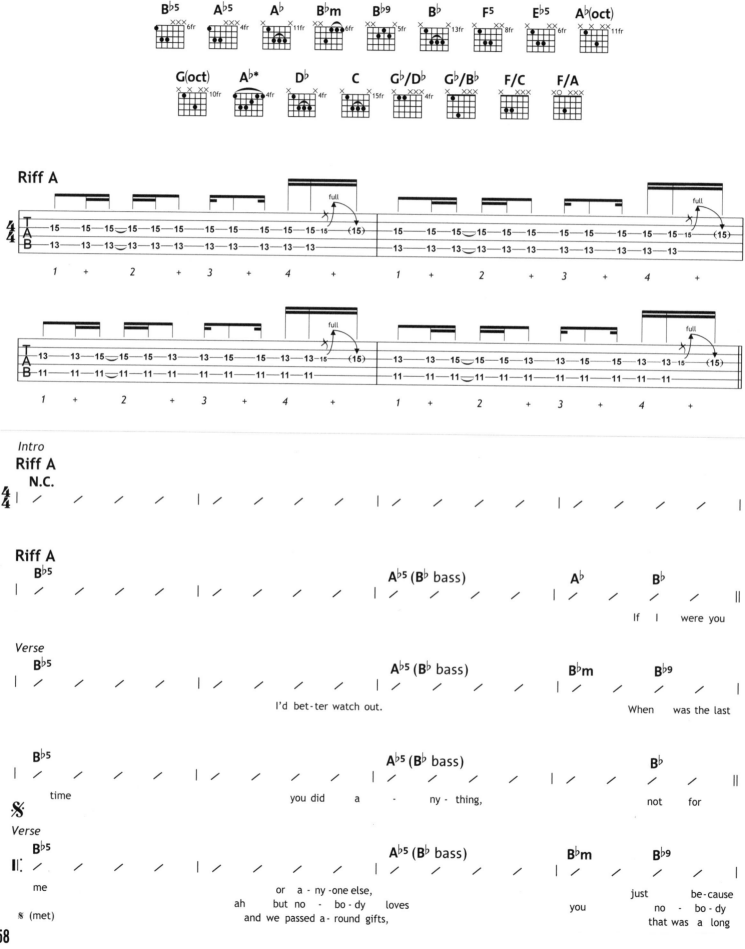

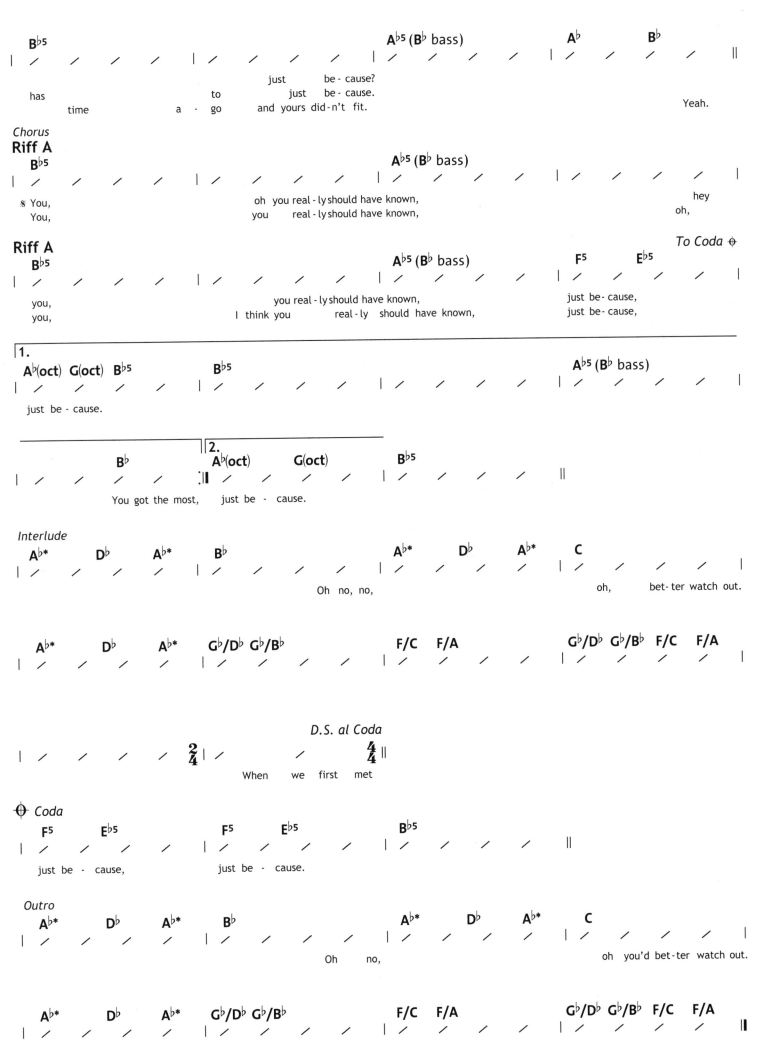

LIVE AND LET DIE

Words & Music by Linda McCartney & Paul McCartney

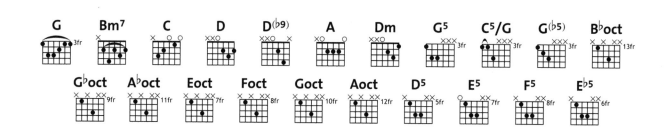

Original recording: tune gtr. down ½ step (1 semitone)

Riff A

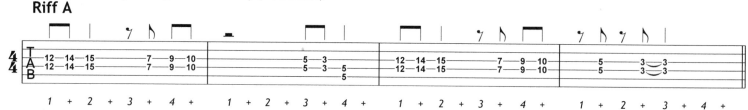

Half time
Verse

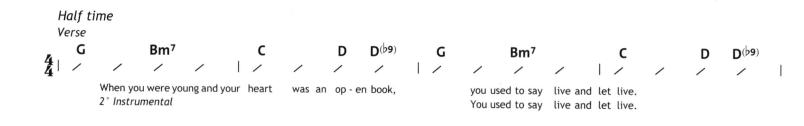

When you were young and your heart   was an op-en book,   you used to say live and let live.
2° Instrumental   You used to say live and let live.

But if this ev-er chang-in' world in which we live in makes you give in and cry;   say live and let
But if this ev-er chang-in' world in which we live in makes you give in and cry;   say live and let die.

die.   Live and let   die.
                                               Live and let   die.

Double time
Interlude 1

Riff A

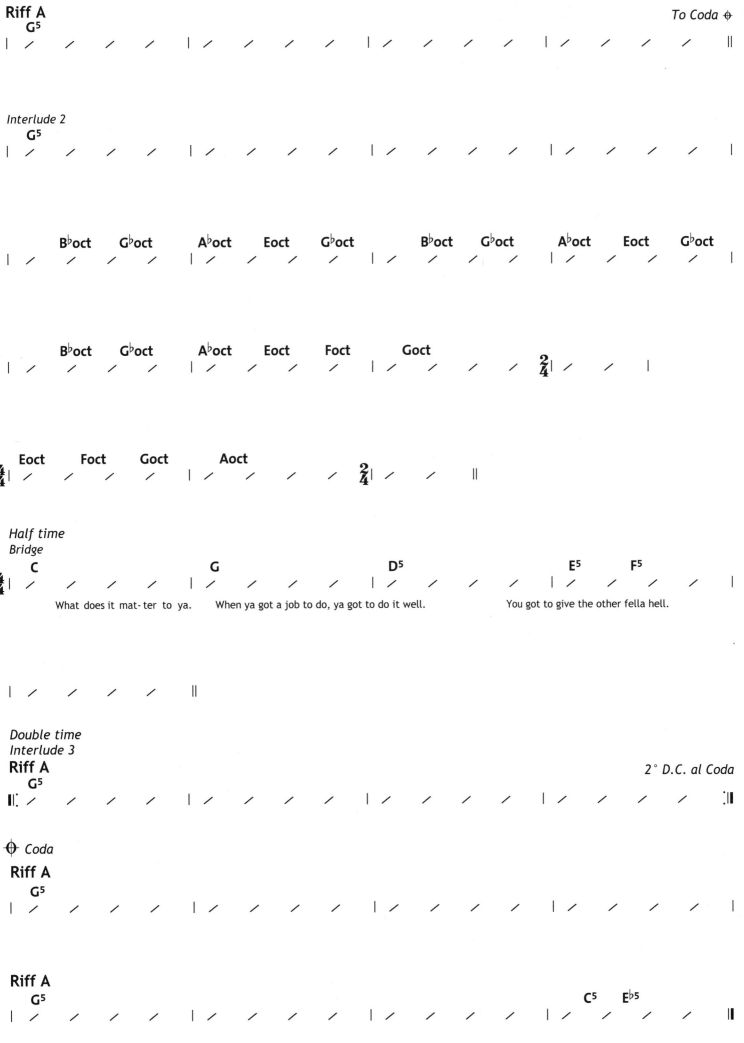

MEIN HERZ BRENNT

Words & Music by Richard Kruspe, Till Lindemann, Paul Landers, Oliver Riedel,
Doktor Lorenz & Christopher Schneider

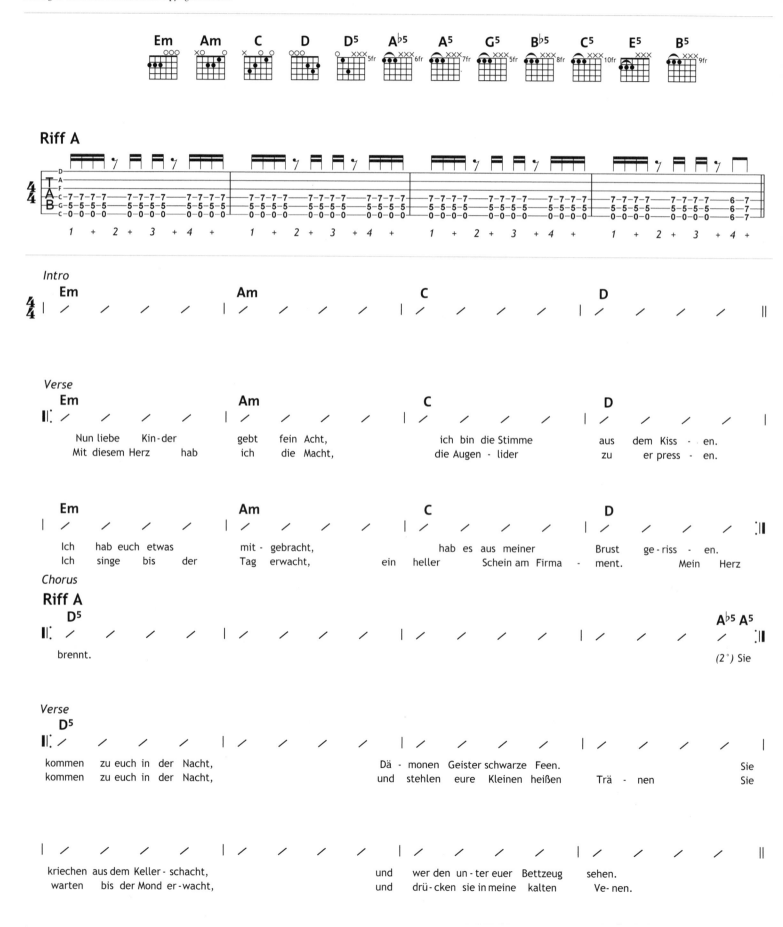

Pre Chorus

| D⁵ | | G⁵ | | B♭⁵ | | A⁵ | |

Nun liebe Kin-der gebt fein Acht, ich bin die Stimme aus dem Kiss - en.
Nun liebe Kin-der gebt fein Acht, ich bin die Stimme aus dem Kiss - en.

| D⁵ | | G⁵ | | B♭⁵ | | A⁵ | |

Ich hab euch etwas mit-ge - bracht, ein heller Schein am Firma - ment. Mein Herz
Ich singe bis der Tag erwacht, ein heller Schein am Firma - ment. Mein Herz

Chorus

Riff A

| D⁵ | | | | A♭⁵ A⁵ |

|1.

brennt. Mein Herz brennt. Sie

|2.

| (D⁵) | A♭⁵ A⁵ |

Mein Herz

Riff A

| D⁵ | | | | A♭⁵ A⁵ |

brennt. Mein Herz brennt.

Bridge

| E⁵ | Am | C | D |

Solo

| E⁵ | A⁵ | C⁵ | D⁵ |

|1.

| E⁵ | A⁵ | C⁵ | B⁵ |

|2.

| D⁵ |

Mein Herz

Chorus

Riff A

| D⁵ | | | | A♭⁵ A⁵ |

brennt. Mein Herz brennt. Mein Herz

Riff A

| D⁵ | | | | A♭⁵ A⁵ |

brennt. Mein Herz brennt.

MONEY FOR NOTHING

Words & Music by Mark Knopfler & Sting

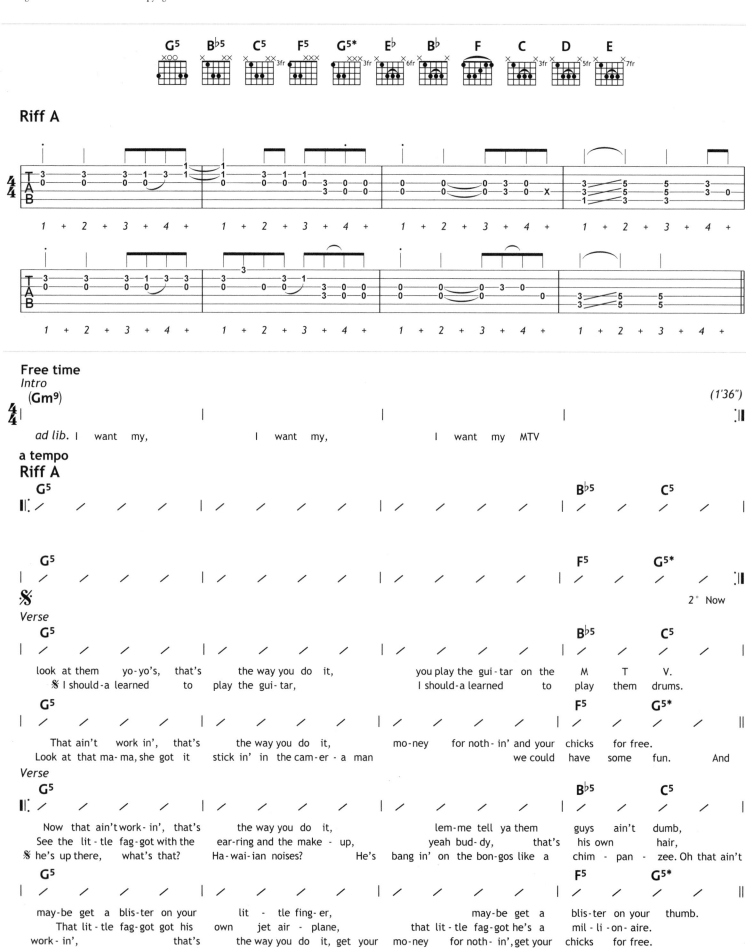

Chorus

E♭ · · · · B♭ · · · · E♭ · · · · F · · · ·

We got - ta in - stall mi - cro - wave ov - ens, cus tom kit - chen de - li - ver - ies.

G5 · · · · · · · · C · · · · D · · · ·

We got - ta move these re - fri - ge - ra - tors, we got - ta move these co - lour T V's.

E · · · · · · · (no repeat D.S.)

Interlude

Riff A

G5 · · · · · · · · · · · · B♭5 · · · C5 · · ·

G5 · · · · · · · · · · · · F5 · · · G5* *To Coda* ⊕

Chorus

E♭ · · · · B♭ · · · · E♭ · · · · F · · · ·

We got - ta in - stall mi - cro - wave ov - ens, cus - tom kit - chen de - li - ver - ies.

G5 · · · · · · · · C · · · · D · · · ·

We got - ta move these re - fri - ge - ra - tors, we got - ta move these co - lour T V's.

E · · · · · · · *D.S. al Coda*

⊕ *Coda*

G5 · · · · · · · · · · · · B♭5 · · · C5 · · ·

Now that ain't work in', that's the way you do it, you play the gui - tar on the M T V.

G5 · · · · · · · · · · · · F5 · · · G5*

That ain't work - in', that's the way you do it, mo - ney for noth - in' and your chicks for free.

Outro

G5 · · · · · · · · · · · · B♭5 · · · C5 · · ·

Mo - ney for no thin' and your chicks for free. Get your

Repeat 4 times

G5 · · · · · · · · · · · · F5 · · · G5*

Mo - ney for no thin' and your chicks for free.

G5 · · · · · · · · · · · · B♭5 · · · C5 · · ·

I want my, I want my, I want my M T V.

Repeat 3 times

G5 · · · · · · · · · · · · F5 · · · G5*

I want my, I want my, I want my M T V.

Guitar solo

G5 · · · · · · · · · · · · B♭5 · · · C5 · · ·

Repeat 6 times to fade

G5 · · · · · · · · · · · · F5 · · · G5*

LOVE WALKED IN

Words & Music by Luke Morley

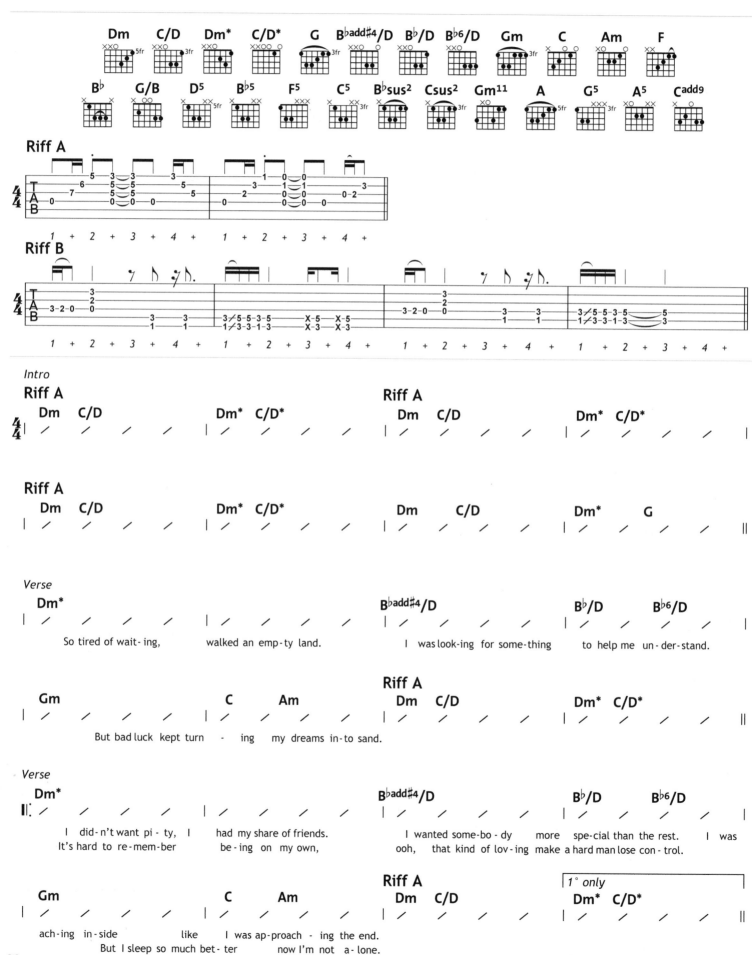

Pre chorus

F / / / / | **C** / / / / |

Just a-bout that mo - ment the tim-ing was so right. you ap -
So pro mise me ba - by you're al-ways gon - na stay. I don't

Dm* / **C/D** / / | **Dm*** / **C/D** / |

peared like a vi - sion sent down to my life.
think I could take it see-ing you walk a - way.

B♭ / / / / | **G/B** / / / ‖

I thought I was dream - ing when I saw you that night That's when
You don't need to doubt it, I re - mem - ber that day. That's when

Chorus

D⁵ / **B♭⁵** / / | **F⁵** / **C⁵** / |

love walked in through my door, that fa -
love walked in through my door, I found

D⁵ / **B♭⁵** / / | **F⁵** / **C⁵** |

mi - li - ar feel - ing I had once be - fore.
just what I want - ed but I got so much more.

D⁵ / **B♭⁵** / / | **F⁵** / **C⁵** / |

Love walked in through my door, and it felt so
Love walked in through my door, and it felt so

1.

B♭sus² / / / / | / / / / |

strange.

Riff A

Dm / **C/D** / / | **Dm*** / **C/D*** / ‖

2.

B♭sus² / / / **Csus²** / / / | **Gm¹¹** / / / **A** / / / ‖

strange. Like a long lost friend that had-n't changed, giv-ing me hope a-gain. Love walked in.

Bridge

Riff B

Dm* / / / **F⁵** / / / **G⁵** / / | **Dm*** / / / **B♭⁵** / **C⁵** / |

Love walked in.

Riff B

Dm* / / / **F⁵** / / / **G⁵** / / | **Dm*** / / / **B♭⁵** / **C⁵** / ‖

Love.

Guitar solo

B♭⁵ / / / / / / / | **C⁵** / **D⁵** / / / / | **C⁵** / / / / |

B♭⁵ / / / / / / / | **F⁵** / / / / | **C⁵** / **A⁵** / / / ‖

67

Interlude
Riff A

Dm C/D   Dm* C/D*   **Riff A** Dm C/D   Dm* C/D*

| ╱ ╱ ╱ ╱ | ╱ ╱ ╱ ╱ | ╱ ╱ ╱ ╱ | ╱ ╱ ╱ ╱ ||

Pre chorus

F   C

| ╱ ╱ ╱ ╱ | ╱ ╱ ╱ ╱ |

Just a - bout that mo - ment the tim - ing was so right you ap -

Dm*   C/D   Dm*   C/D

| ╱ ╱ ╱ ╱ | ╱ ╱ ╱ ╱ |

- peared like a vi - sion sent down to my life

B♭   G/B

| ╱ ╱ ╱ ╱ | ╱ ╱ ╱ ╱ ||

I thought I was dream - ing when I saw you that night. That's when

Chorus

D5   B♭5   F5   C5

| ╱ ╱ ╱ ╱ | ╱ ╱ ╱ ╱ |

love walked in through my door that fa -

D5   B♭5   F5   C5

| ╱ ╱ ╱ ╱ | ╱ ╱ ╱ ╱ |

mi - li - ar feel - ing I had once be - fore

D5   B♭5   F5   C5

| ╱ ╱ ╱ ╱ | ╱ ╱ ╱ ╱ |

Love walked in through my door. Oh,

D5   B♭5   F5   C5

| ╱ ╱ ╱ ╱ | ╱ ╱ ╱ ╱ |

love walked in through my door.

D5   B♭5   F5   C5

| ╱ ╱ ╱ ╱ | ╱ ╱ ╱ ╱ |

That fa - mi - liar feel - ing I had it once be - fore.

D5   B♭5   F5   C5

| ╱ ╱ ╱ ╱ | ╱ ╱ ╱ ╱ |

Love walked in through my door. And it felt so

B♭sus2   Csus2

| ╱ ╱ ╱ ╱ | ╱ ╱ ╱ ╱ |

strange. Like a long lost friend that had - n't

Gm11   A

| ╱ ╱ ╱ ╱ | ╱ ╱ ╱ ╱ ||

changed, giv - ing me hope a - gain. Ooh.

Bridge
Riff B

Dm*   F5   G5   Dm*   B♭5   C5

| ╱ ╱ ╱ ╱ | ╱ ╱ ╱ | ╱ ╱ ╱ ╱ | ╱ ╱ ╱ ╱ |

Love walked in. Ooh.

Riff B

Dm*   F5   G5   Dm*   B♭5   C5

| ╱ ╱ ╱ ╱ | ╱ ╱ ╱ | ╱ ╱ ╱ ╱ | ╱ ╱ ╱ ╱ ||

Love walked in. Love.

Guitar solo
Riff B

Dm*   F5   G5   Dm*   B♭5   C5   *Play 3 times*

||: ╱ ╱ ╱ ╱ | ╱ ╱ ╱ | ╱ ╱ ╱ ╱ | ╱ ╱ ╱ ╱ :||

Love walked in.

(Dm*)

| ╱ ╱ ╱ ╱ | ╱ ╱ ╱ ╱ ||

MY SACRIFICE

Words & Music by Mark Tremonti & Scott Stapp

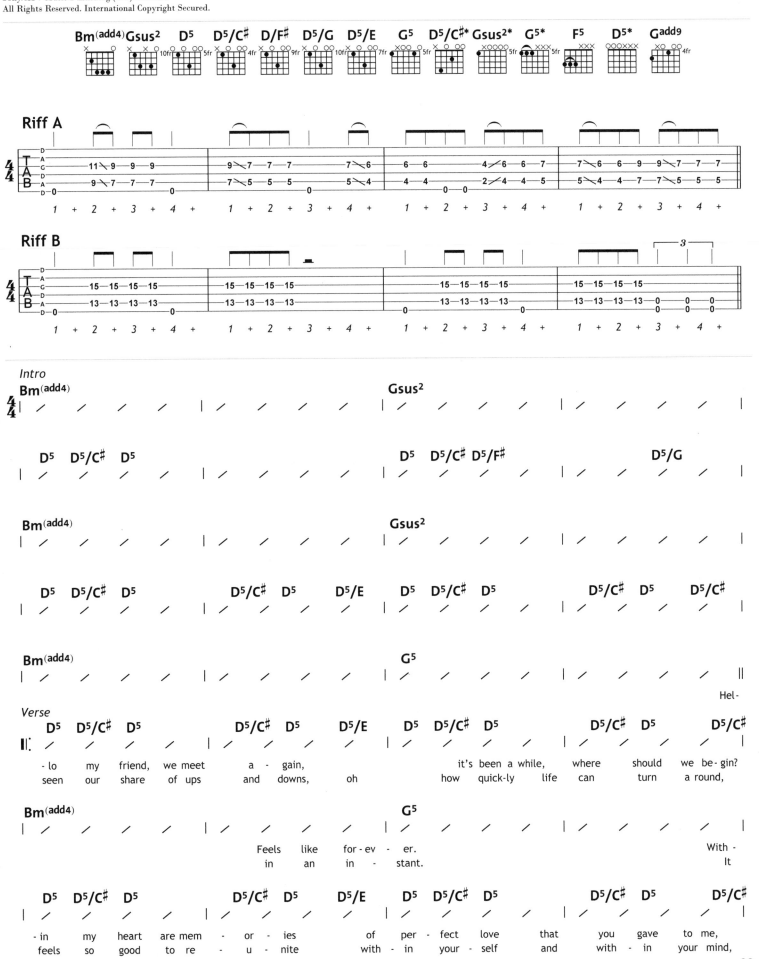

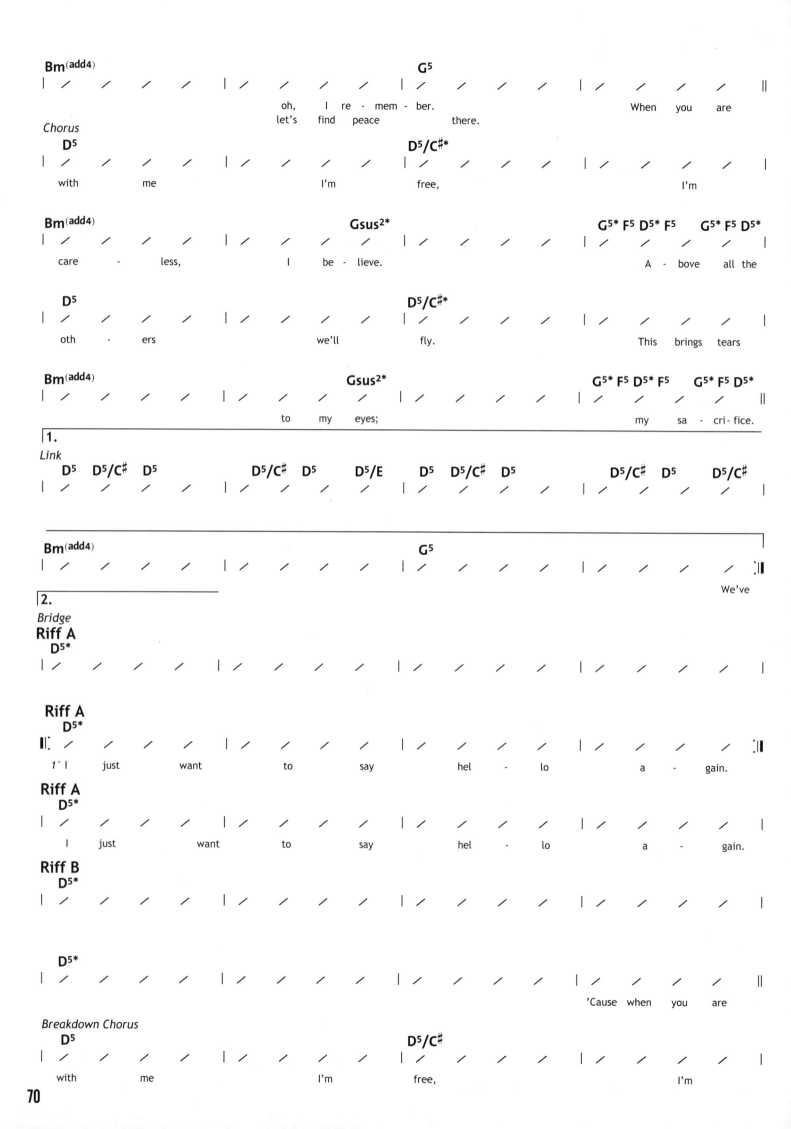

Bm(add4)   G5
| / / / / | / / / / | / / / / | / / / ||
                           oh, I re - mem - ber.   When you are
                           let's find peace   there.

Chorus
    D5   D5/C#*
| / / / / | / / / / | / / / / | / / / |
    with   me   I'm   free,   I'm

Bm(add4)   Gsus2*   G5* F5 D5* F5   G5* F5 D5*
| / / / / | / / / / | / / / / | / / / / |
    care - less,   I   be - lieve.   A - bove all the

    D5   D5/C#*
| / / / / | / / / / | / / / / | / / / / |
    oth - ers   we'll   fly.   This brings tears

Bm(add4)   Gsus2*   G5* F5 D5* F5   G5* F5 D5*
| / / / / | / / / / | / / / / | / / / ||
                    to   my eyes;   my sa - cri - fice.

|1.
Link
    D5   D5/C# D5   D5/C# D5   D5/E   D5   D5/C# D5   D5/C# D5   D5/C#
| / / / / | / / / / | / / / / | / / / / |

Bm(add4)   G5
| / / / / | / / / / | / / / / | / / / / :||
                                                                      We've

|2.
Bridge
Riff A
    D5*
| / / / / | / / / / | / / / / | / / / / |

Riff A
    D5*
||: / / / / | / / / / | / / / / | / / / / :||
  1° | just   want   to   say   hel - lo   a - gain.

Riff A
    D5*
| / / / / | / / / / | / / / / | / / / / |
    I   just   want   to   say   hel - lo   a - gain.

Riff B
    D5*
| / / / / | / / / / | / / / / | / / / / |

    D5*
| / / / / | / / / / | / / / / | / / / ||
                                                  'Cause when you are

Breakdown Chorus
    D5   D5/C#
| / / / / | / / / / | / / / / | / / / / |
    with   me   I'm   free,   I'm

70

Bm(add4) / / / / | / / / / | **Gsus²** / / / | **Gadd9** / / | **Gsus²*** / / / |

care - less,   I   be - lieve.   A - bove   all   the

D⁵ / / / / | / / / / | **D⁵/C♯** / / / | / / / | / / / |

oth - ers   we'll   fly.   This   brings   tears

Bm(add4) / / / / | / / / / | **Gsus²** / / / | **N.C.** / / / | / / / / |

to   my   eyes;   'Cause   when   you   are

Chorus
D⁵ / / / / | / / / / | **D⁵/C♯** / / / | / / / | / / / |

with   me,   I'm   free,   I'm

Bm(add4) / / / / | / / / / | **Gsus²** / / / | **G⁵* F⁵ D⁵* F⁵** / / | **G⁵* F⁵ D⁵*** / / |

care - less,   I   be - lieve.   A - bove   all   the

D⁵ / / / / | / / / / | **D⁵/C♯** / / / | / / / | / / / |

oth - ers   we'll   fly.   This   brings   tears

Bm(add4) / / / / | / / / / | **Gsus²** / / / | **G⁵* F⁵ D⁵* F⁵** / / | **G⁵* F⁵ D⁵*** / / ‖

End   to   my   eyes;   my   sa - cri - fice.

Riff A
D⁵* / / / / | / / / / | / / / | / / / | / / / |

My   sa - cri - fice.

Riff A
D⁵* / / / / | / / / / | / / / | / / / | / / / |

I   just   want   to   say   hel - lo   a - gain.

Riff A
D⁵* / / / / | / / / / | / / / | / / / | / / / |

I   just   want   to   say   hel - lo   a - gain.

Riff B
D⁵* / / / / | / / / / | / / / | / / / | / / / |

My   sa - cri - fice.

D⁵* / / / / | / / / / | / / / | / / / | / / / |

D⁵ / / / / | / / / / | **D⁵/C♯*** / / / | / / / | / / / |

Bm(add4) / / / / | / / / / | **Gsus²*** / / / | **D⁵/C♯** / / / | *Fade out* / ‖

NO ONE KNOWS

Words & Music by Josh Homme, Nick Oliveri & Mark Lanegan

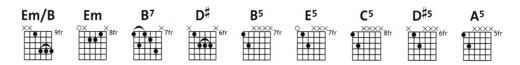

Original recording: tune gtr. down 2 whole steps (2 tones)

Riff A

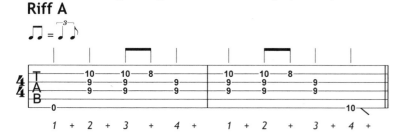

Riff B

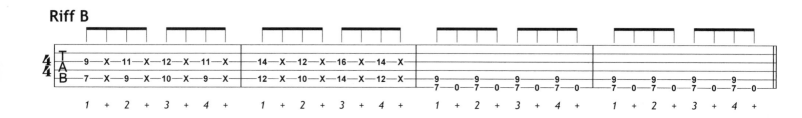

Intro

Riff A   **Riff A**

Verse

We   get   some   rules   through   to   fol -   low,
I   jour - ney   through   the   de   -   sert

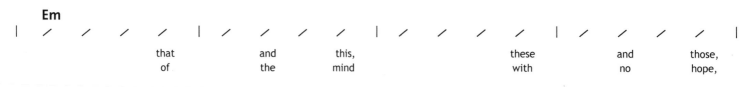

that   and   this,   these   and   those,
of   the   mind   with   no   hope,

B⁷ | ∕ ∕ ∕ ∕ | ∕ ∕ ∕ ∕ | **D♯** ∕ ∕ ∕ ∕ | ∕ ∕ ∕ ∕ |

no one knows.
I fol - low.

Riff A
Em | ∕ ∕ ∕ ∕ | ∕ ∕ ∕ ∕ | **Riff A** ∕ ∕ ∕ ∕ | ∕ ∕ ∕ ∕ |

𝄋
Em | ∕ ∕ ∕ ∕ | ∕ ∕ ∕ ∕ | ∕ ∕ ∕ ∕ | ∕ ∕ ∕ ∕ |

We get these pills to swal - low,
I drift a - long the o - cean,
𝄋 Hea - ven smiles a - bove me,

Em | ∕ ∕ ∕ ∕ | ∕ ∕ ∕ ∕ | ∕ ∕ ∕ ∕ | ∕ ∕ ∕ ∕ |

how they stick in your throat,
dead life - boats in the sun,
what a gift there be - low,

B⁷ | ∕ ∕ ∕ ∕ | ∕ ∕ ∕ ∕ | **D♯** ∕ ∕ ∕ ∕ | ∕ ∕ ∕ ∕ |

tastes like gold.
and come un - done.
but no - one knows.

Riff A
Em | ∕ ∕ ∕ ∕ | ∕ ∕ ∕ ∕ | **Riff A** ∕ ∕ ∕ ∕ | ∕ ∕ ∕ ∕ |

Oh, what you do
Plea - sant - ly cav -
A gift that you give

B⁷ | ∕ ∕ ∕ ∕ | ∕ ∕ ∕ ∕ | **D♯** ∕ ∕ ∕ ∕ | *To Coda* ⊕ ∕ ∕ ∕ |

to me, no - one knows.
ing in. I come un - done.
to me, no - one knows.

Riff A
Em | ∕ ∕ ∕ ∕ | ∕ ∕ ∕ ∕ | **Riff A** ∕ ∕ ∕ ∕ | ∕ ∕ ∕ ∕ ‖

And I

Chorus
Riff B
N.C. | ∕ ∕ ∕ ∕ | ∕ ∕ ∕ ∕ | ∕ ∕ ∕ ∕ | ∕ ∕ ∕ ∕ |

re - al - ize you're mine, in -

Riff B
N.C. | ∕ ∕ ∕ ∕ | ∕ ∕ ∕ ∕ | ∕ ∕ ∕ ∕ | ∕ ∕ ∕ ∕ |

- deed a fool of mine. And I

Riff B

N.C. B^5

| / / / / | / / / / | / / / / | / / / / |

re - al - ize   you're   mine,   in -

Riff B

N.C. B^5

| / / / / | / / / / | / / / / | / / / / |

- deed   a   fool   of   mine.   Ah.

1.

Riff A   **Riff A**

Em*

| / / / / | / / / / | / / / / | / / / / :||

2.

Interlude $\overline{3}$ $\overline{3}$

E^5 B^5 C^5 $D^{\#5}$ B^5 A^5 B^5

| / / / / | / / / / | / / / / | / / / / |

                                      $\overline{3}$ $\overline{3}$

E^5 B^5 C^5 $D^{\#5}$ B^5 A^5 B^5

| / / / / | / / / / | / / / / | / / / / |

$\overline{3}$ $\overline{3}$ $\overline{3}$ $\overline{3}$ $\overline{3}$ $\overline{3}$

B^5 C^5 $D^{\#5}$ B^5 A^5 B^5 B^5 C^5 $D^{\#5}$ B^5 A^5 B^5 B^5 C^5 $D^{\#5}$ B^5 A^5 B^5

| / / / / | / / / / | / / / / ||

Link (Bass solo)

E^5

| / / / / | / / / / | / / / / | / / / / ||

Guitar solo

(Em)   *Repeat 4 times*

||: / / / / | / / / / | / / / / | / / / / :||

Link (Bass solo)

(Em)   *D.S. al Coda*

| / / / / | / / / / | / / / / | / / / / ||

$\oplus$ *Coda*

Em/B

| / / / / | / / / / | / / / / ||

PAPERCUT

Words & Music by Chester Bennington, Mike Shinoda, Rob Bourdon, Joseph Hahn & Brad Delson

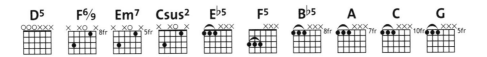

Original recording: tune gtr. down ½ step (1 semitone)

Riff A

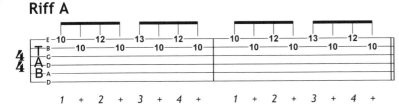

Riff B

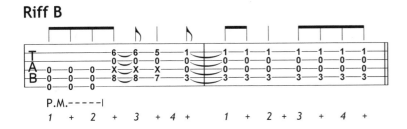

Intro

2 bars Drums

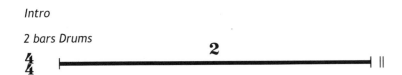

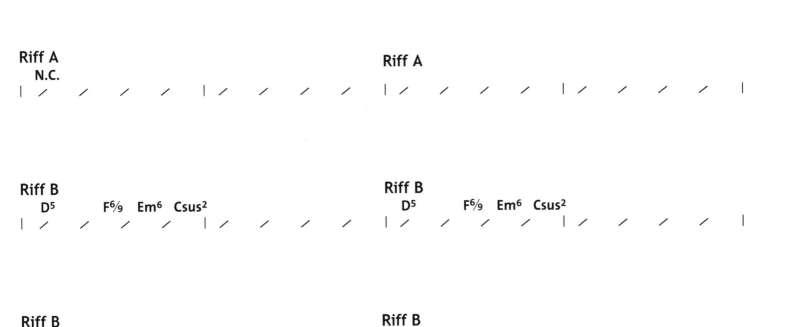

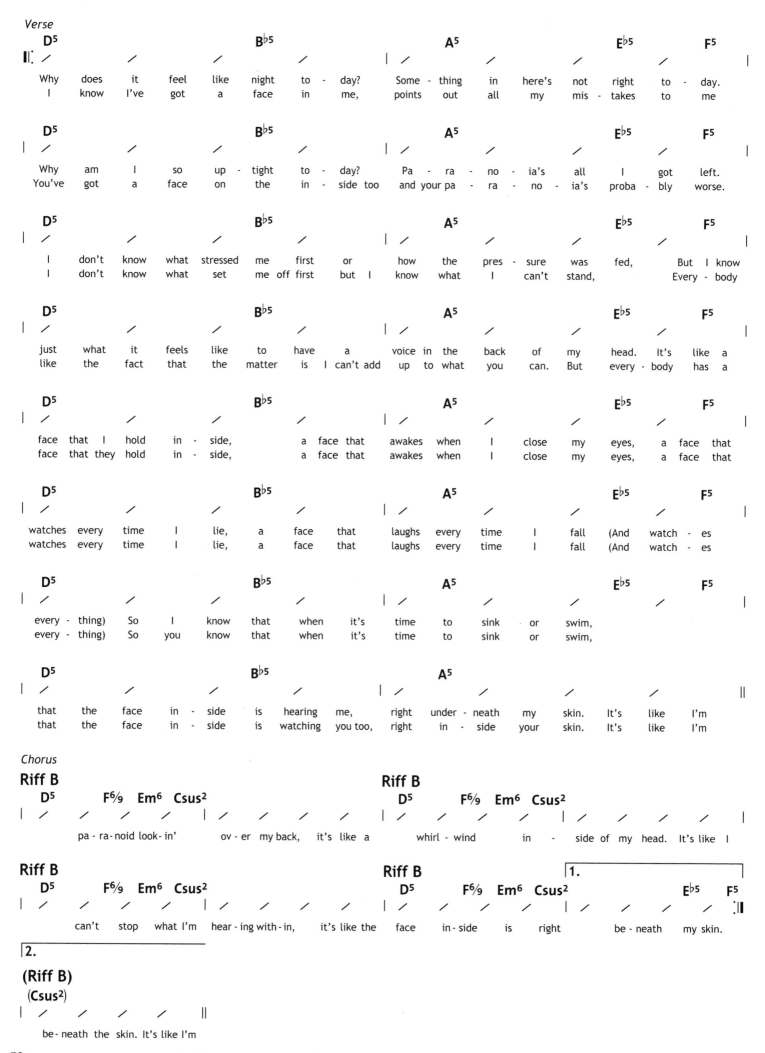

Verse

D⁵　　　　　　　　　　　　B♭5　　　　　　　　　　A⁵　　　　　　　　　　E♭5　　　　F⁵

Why does it feel like night to - day? Some - thing in here's not right to - day.
I know I've got a face in me, points out all my mis - takes to me

D⁵　　　　　　　　　　　　B♭5　　　　　　　　　　A⁵　　　　　　　　　　E♭5　　　　F⁵

Why am I so up - tight to - day? Pa - ra - no - ia's all I got left.
You've got a face on the in - side too and your pa - ra - no - ia's proba - bly worse.

D⁵　　　　　　　　　　　　B♭5　　　　　　　　　　A⁵　　　　　　　　　　E♭5　　　　F⁵

I don't know what stressed me first or how the pres - sure was fed, But I know
I don't know what set me off first but I know what I can't stand, Every - body

D⁵　　　　　　　　　　　　B♭5　　　　　　　　　　A⁵　　　　　　　　　　E♭5　　　　F⁵

just what it feels like to have a voice in the back of my head. It's like a
like the fact that the matter is I can't add up to what you can. But every - body has a

D⁵　　　　　　　　　　　　B♭5　　　　　　　　　　A⁵　　　　　　　　　　E♭5　　　　F⁵

face that I hold in - side, a face that awakes when I close my eyes, a face that
face that they hold in - side, a face that awakes when I close my eyes, a face that

D⁵　　　　　　　　　　　　B♭5　　　　　　　　　　A⁵　　　　　　　　　　E♭5　　　　F⁵

watches every time I lie, a face that laughs every time I fall (And watch - es
watches every time I lie, a face that laughs every time I fall (And watch - es

D⁵　　　　　　　　　　　　B♭5　　　　　　　　　　A⁵　　　　　　　　　　E♭5　　　　F⁵

every - thing) So I know that when it's time to sink - or swim,
every - thing) So you know that when it's time to sink or swim,

D⁵　　　　　　　　　　　　B♭5　　　　　　　　　　A⁵

that the face in - side is hearing me, right under - neath my skin. It's like I'm
that the face in - side is watching you too, right in - side your skin. It's like I'm

Chorus

Riff B　　　　　　　　　　　　　　　　　　　　　　　**Riff B**

D⁵　　　　F⁶/₉ Em⁶ Csus²　　　　　　　　　　D⁵　　　F⁶/₉ Em⁶ Csus²

pa - ra - noid look - in' ov - er my back, it's like a whirl - wind in - side of my head. It's like I

Riff B　　　　　　　　　　　　　　　　　　　　　**Riff B**　　　　　　　　　1.

D⁵　　　　F⁶/₉ Em⁶ Csus²　　　　　　　　　　D⁵　　　F⁶/₉ Em⁶ Csus²　　　　E♭5　F⁵

can't stop what I'm hear - ing with - in, it's like the face in - side is right be - neath my skin.

2.

(Riff B)

(Csus²)

be - neath the skin. It's like I'm

Chorus

Riff B

D5   F6/9 Em6 Csus2   **Riff B**   D5   F6/9 Em6 Csus2

| / / / / | / / / / | / / / / | / / / / |

pa - ra - noid   look - in' ov - er my back,   it's like a   whirl - wind   in - side of my head.   It' like I

Riff B

D5   F6/9 Em6 Csus2   **Riff B**   D5   F6/9 Em6 Csus2   Eb5   F5

| / / / / | / / / / | / / / / | / / / / ‖

can't   stop   what I'm   hear - ing with - in,   it's like the   face   in - side   is   right   be - neath   my   skin.

Interlude

w/Riff A

D5   Eb5 F5 D5   Eb5 F5

| / / / / | / / / / | / / / / | / / / / |

The face in - side is   right be -neath the skin.   The face in - side is   right be - neath the skin.

D5   Eb5 F5 D5

| / / / / | / / / / | / / / / | / / / / ‖

The face in - side is   right be -neath the skin.   Yeah the

Outro

Bb5   C5   G5

‖: / / / / | / / / / | / / / / | / / / / |

sun   goes   down,
(Vocal Fig. 1)

Bb5   C5   G5

| / / / / | / / / / | / / / / | / / / / :‖

I   feel   the light   be - tray   me.   The (It's like I'm)

Bb5   C5   G5

| / / / / | / / / / | / / / / | / / / / |

pa - ra - noid   look - in' ov - er my back, it's like a   whirl - wind   in - side of my head.   It's like I

Bb5   C5   G5

| / / / / | / / / / | / / / / | / / / / |

can't   stop   what I'm   hear - ing with - in, it's like the   face   in - side   is   right   be - neath my skin.It's like I'm
(Vocal Fig. 1 cont. sim.)

Bb5   C5   G5

| / / / / | / / / / | / / / / | / / / / |

pa - ra - noid   look - in' ov - er my back, it' like a   whirl - wind   in - side of my head.   It's like I

Bb5   C5   Bb5   C5

| / / / / | / / / / | / / / / | / / / / |

can't   stop   what I'm   hear - ing with - in,   it's like I   can't   stop   what I'm   hear - ing with - in, it's like

Bb5   C5   G5   Eb5 F5

| / / / / | / / / / | / / / / | / / / / |

can't   stop   what I'm   hear - ing with - in,   it's like the   face   in - side   is   right   be - neath   my   skin.

D5

| / / / / | ‖

PARANOID

Words & Music by Ozzy Osbourne, Tony Iommi, Terry 'Geezer' Butler & Bill Ward

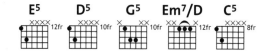

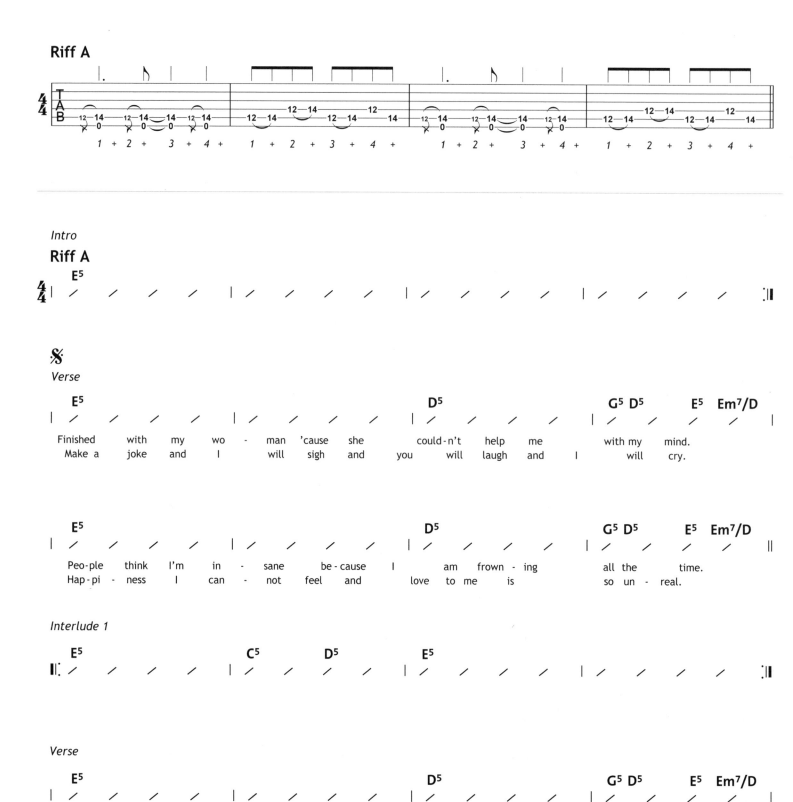

E5   **D5**

To Coda

| **E5** | | | | **D5** | | | **G5 D5** | **E5 Em7/D** |

Think I'll lose my mind if I don't find some - thing to pa - ci - fy.
I tell you to en - joy life I wish I could but it's too late.

Bridge
| **E5** | | | | **D5** | | | | |

Can you help me oc - cu - py my brain?

| **E5** | | | | **D5** | | | | |

Whoa oh yeah.

Interlude 2
| **E5** | | | | **D5** | | | **G5 D5** | **E5 Em7/D** |

Verse
| **E5** | | | | **D5** | | | **G5 D5** | **E5 Em7/D** |

I need some - one to show me the things in life that I can't find.

| **E5** | | | | **D5** | | | **G5 D5** | **E5 Em7/D** |

I can't see the things that make true hap - pi - ness, I must be blind.

Guitar solo   *Play 4 times*
| **E5** | | | | **D5** | | | **G5 D5** | **E5 Em7/D** |

Interlude 3   *2° D.S. al Coda*
| **E5** | | | | **D5** | | | **G5 D5** | **E5 Em7/D** |

Coda
| **E5** | | | | **D5** | | | **G5 D5** | **E5 Em7/D** |

| **E5** | | | | **D5** | | | **G5** | **E5** |

79

PLUG IN BABY

Words & Music by Matthew Bellamy

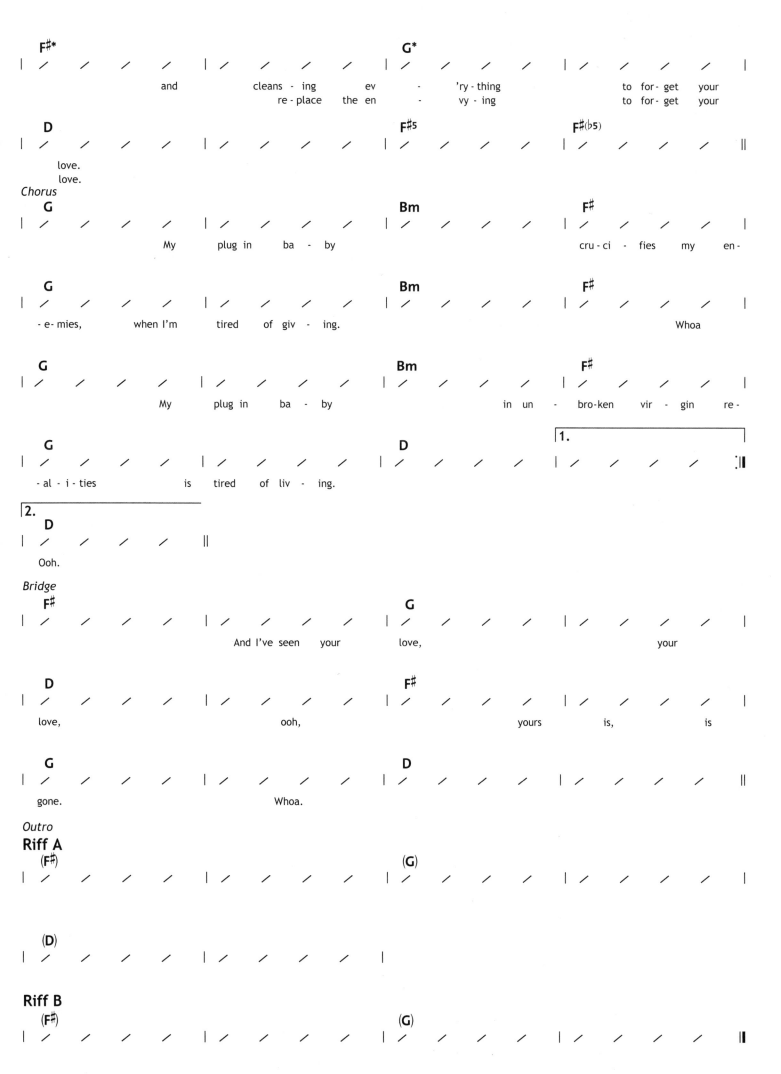

POUR SOME SUGAR ON ME

Words & Music by Steve Clark, Pete Willis, Rick Savage, Joe Elliott & Robert John 'Mutt' Lange

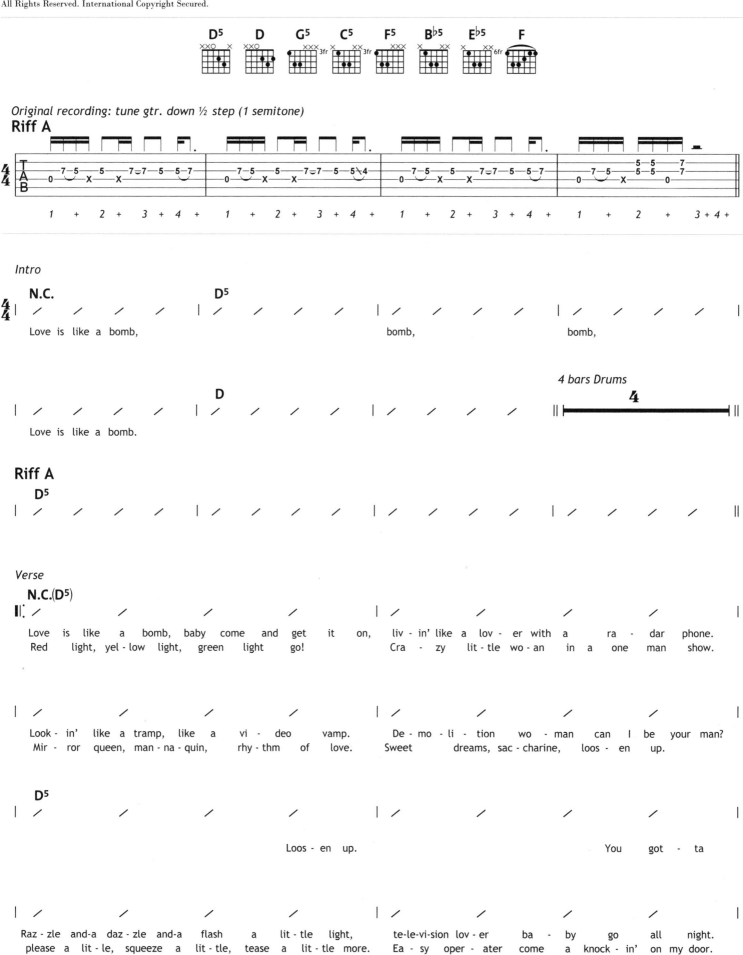

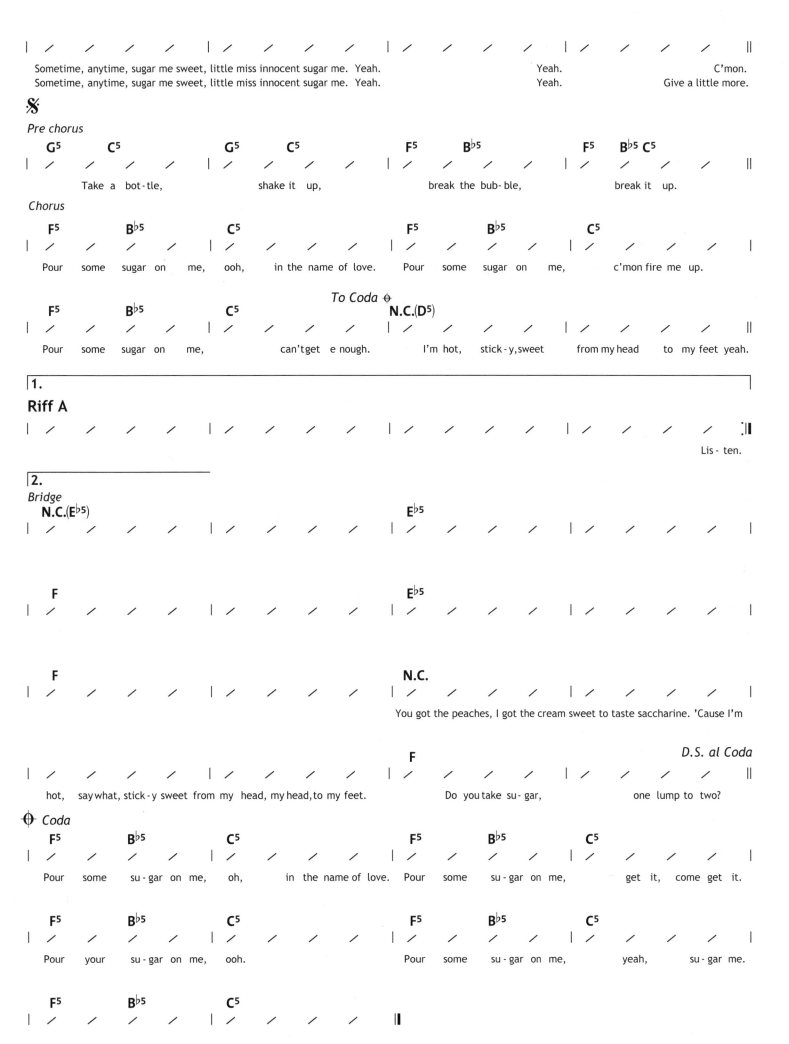

REBEL REBEL

Words & Music by David Bowie

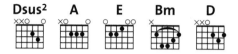

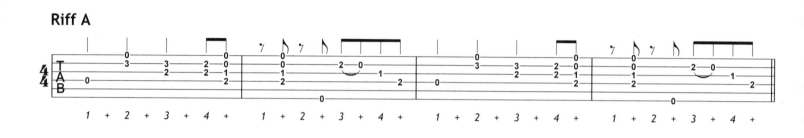

Riff A

Intro

Riff A

Dsus² / / / / A E / / / / Dsus² / / / / A E / / / /   *Repeat 4 times*

Verse

Riff A

Dsus² / / / / A E / / / / Dsus² / / / / A E / / / /

You've got your moth-er in a whirl, she's not sure if you're a boy or a girl.

Riff A

Dsus² / / / / A E / / / / Dsus² / / / / A E / / / /

Hey babe, your hair's al - right, hey babe, let's go out to-night.

Riff A

Dsus² / / / / A E / / / / Dsus² / / / / A E / / / /

You like me, and I like it all, we like danc - ing and we look di - vine.

Riff A

Dsus² / / / / A E / / / / Dsus² / / / / A E / / / /

You love bands when they play it hard, you want more and you want it fast.

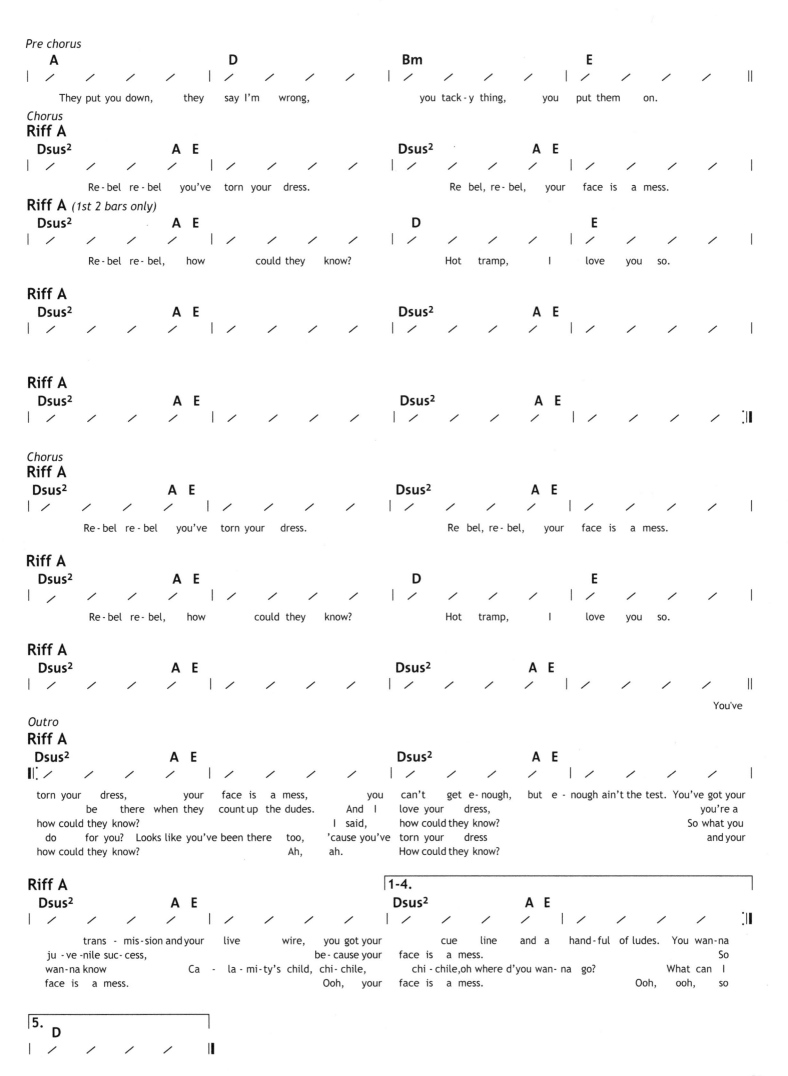

Pre chorus

A   D   Bm   E

They put you down,   they   say I'm   wrong,   you tack - y thing,   you   put them   on.

Chorus
Riff A

Dsus²   **A E**   **Dsus²**   **A E**

Re - bel   re - bel   you've   torn your   dress.   Re - bel, re - bel,   your   face is   a mess.

Riff A *(1st 2 bars only)*

Dsus²   **A E**   **D**   **E**

Re - bel   re - bel,   how   could they   know?   Hot   tramp,   I   love   you   so.

Riff A

Dsus²   **A E**   **Dsus²**   **A E**

Riff A

Dsus²   **A E**   **Dsus²**   **A E**

Chorus
Riff A

Dsus²   **A E**   **Dsus²**   **A E**

Re - bel   re - bel   you've   torn your   dress.   Re - bel, re - bel,   your   face is   a mess.

Riff A

Dsus²   **A E**   **D**   **E**

Re - bel   re - bel,   how   could they   know?   Hot   tramp,   I   love   you   so.

Riff A

Dsus²   **A E**   **Dsus²**   **A E**

You've

Outro
Riff A

Dsus²   **A E**   **Dsus²**   **A E**

torn your   dress,   your   face is a mess,   you   can't   get e- nough,   but e - nough ain't the test. You've got your
       be   there when they   count up the dudes.   And I   love your   dress,   you're a
how could they know?   I said,   how could they know?   So what you
do   for you? Looks like you've been there   too,   'cause you've   torn your   dress   and your
how could they know?   Ah,   ah.   How could they know?

Riff A

Dsus²   **A E**   **1-4.**   **Dsus²**   **A E**

trans - mis-sion and your   live   wire,   you got your   cue   line   and a   hand-ful of ludes. You wan-na
ju -ve -nile suc- cess,   be - cause your   face is   a mess.   So
wan-na know   Ca - la - mi-ty's child, chi - chile,   chi - chile,oh where d'you wan- na   go?   What can I
face is   a mess.   Ooh,   your   face is   a mess.   Ooh,   ooh,   so

5.   **D**

ROADHOUSE BLUES

Words & Music by Jim Morrison, Robbie Krieger, Ray Manzarek & John Densmore

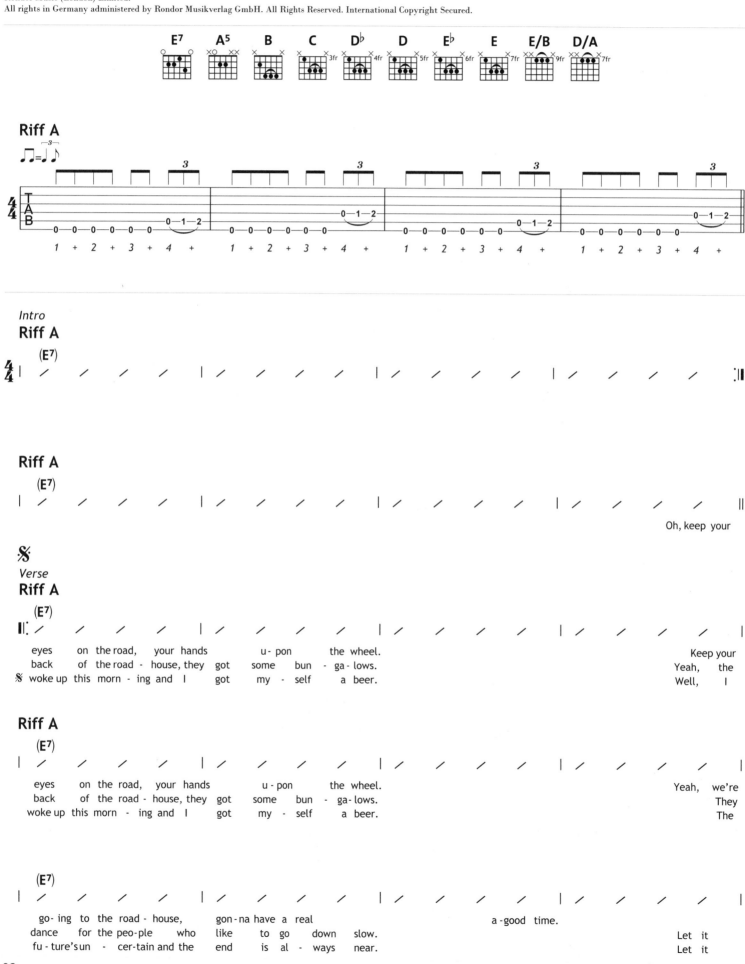

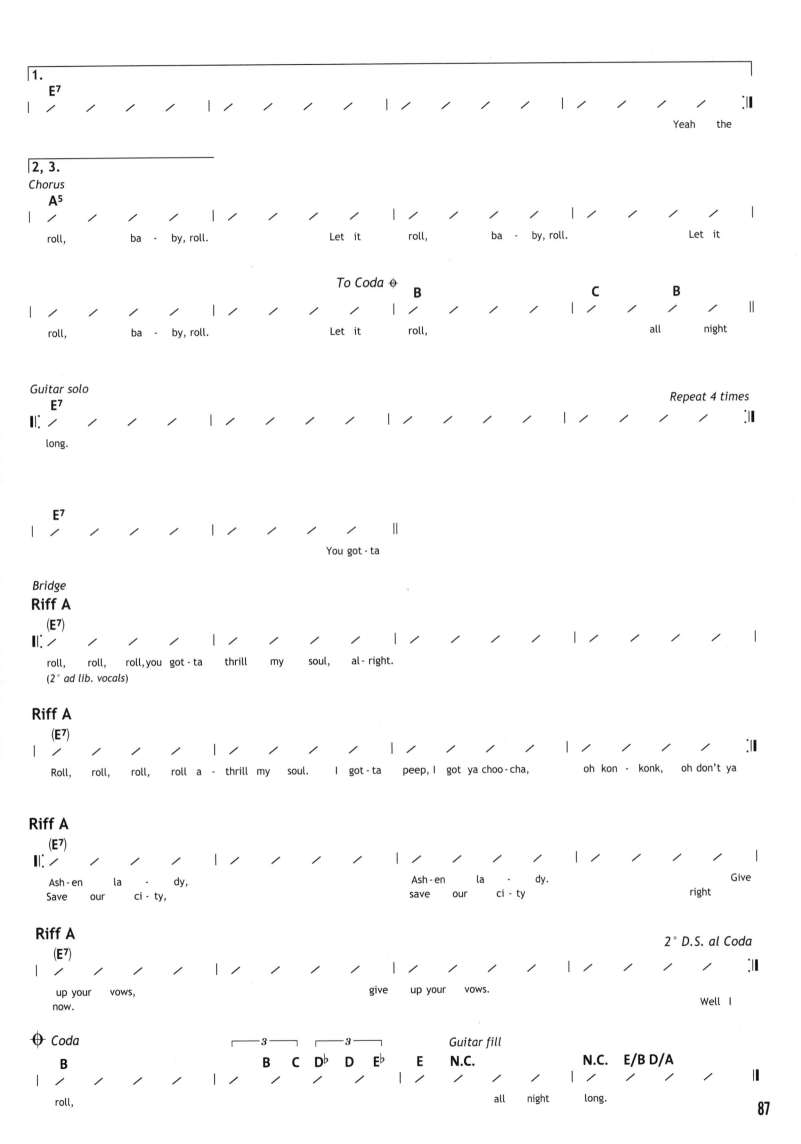

SLITHER

Words & Music by Matt Sorum, Duff 'Rose' McKagan, David Kushner,
Saul Hudson & Scott Weilund

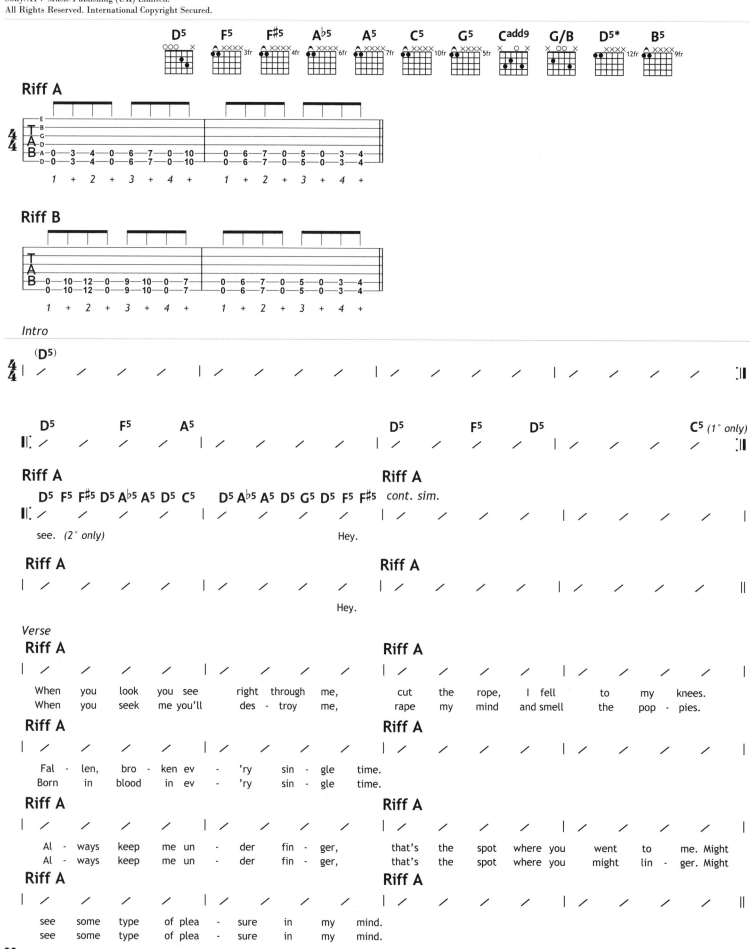

Chorus

D5 · · · · | · · · · | Cadd9 · · · · | · · · ·

Yeah,　　　　he'll come　to　wa - ter,　　　hecomes　to

G/B · · · · | · · · · | D5 · · · · | · · · · :||

wash　a - way　the　sins　of　you　and　I.　This　time　you'll

Chorus

D5 · · · · | · · · · | Cadd9 · · · · | · · · ·

see.　　　Like　ho - ly　wa - ter,　　　it　on - ly

G/B · · · · | · · · · | D5 · · · · | · · · · ||

burns　you fast - er　than　you'll ev - er　dry.　This　time　with

Interlude

(D5) · · · · | · · · · | (C/D) · · · · | · · · ·

me.

(G/D) · · · · | · · · · | (D) · · · · | · · · · ||

Solo

||: D5 · · · · | · · · · | Cadd9 · · · · | · · · ·

┌ 1.

G/B · · · · | · · · · | D5 · · · · | · · · · :||

└ 2.

D5 · · · · ||

Bridge

Riff A
D5 F5 F#5 D5 Ab5 A5 D5 C5　D5 Ab5 A5 D5 G5 D5 F5 F#5 **Riff A** *cont. sim.*
· · · · | · · · · | · · · · | · · · ·

When　you　look　you see　right through　me,　cut　the　rope,　I fell　to　my　knees.

Riff A　　　　　　　**Riff B**
D5 C5 D5* D5 B5 C5 D5 A5　D5 Ab5 A5 D5 G5 D5 F5 F#5
· · · · | · · · · | · · · · | · · · · ||

Born　in blood　in ev - 'ry　sin - gle　time.

Chorus

||: D5 · · · · | · · · · | Cadd9 · · · · | · · · ·

Yeah,　　　　he'll come　to　wa - ter,　　　hecomes　to
see.　　　Like　ho - ly　wa - ter,　　　it　on - ly

G/B · · · · | · · · · | D5 · · · · | · · · · :||

wash　a - way　the　sins　of　you　and　I.　This　time　you'll
burns　you fast - er　than　you'll ev - er　dry.　This　time　with

Outro

Riff A　　　　　　　**Riff A**
· · · · | · · · · | · · · · | · · · ·

me.　　　Hey.　　　　　Hey.

Riff A　　　　　　　**Riff B**
D5 F5 F#5 D5 Ab5 A5 D5 C5　D5 Ab5 A5 D5 G5 D5 F5 F#5　D5 C5 D5* D5 B5 C5 D5 A5　D5 Ab5 A5 D5 G5 D5 F5 F#5
· · · · | · · · · | · · · · | · · · ·

D5 · · · · ||

Hey.

VERTIGO

Words & Music by U2

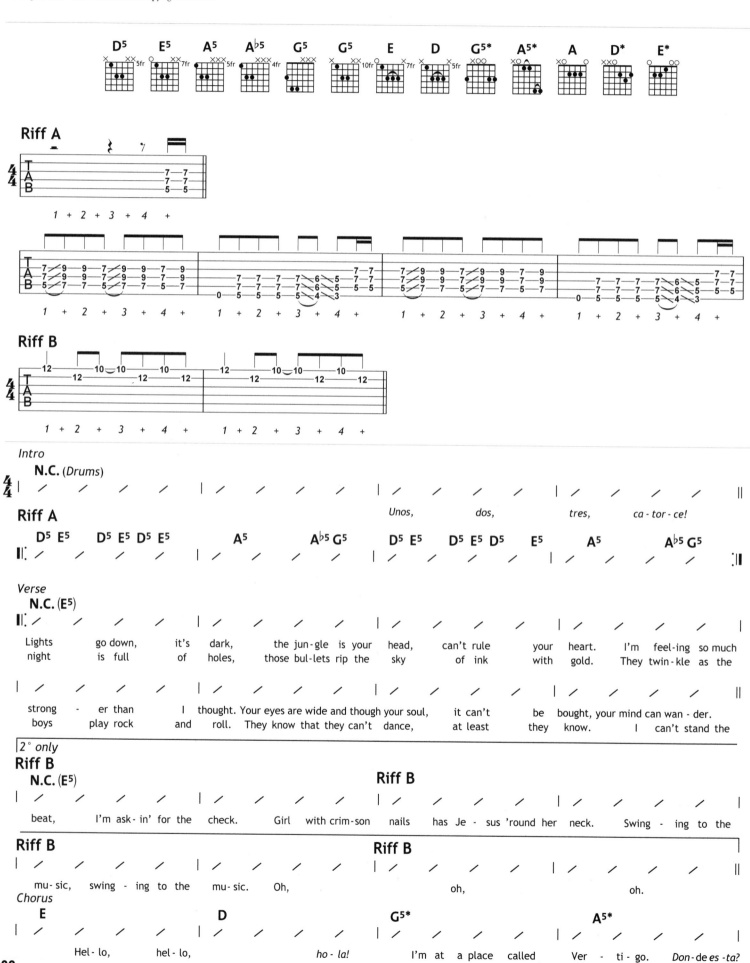

E   D   G5*   A5*

| / / / | / / / | / / / | / / / |

It's ev-'ry-thing I wish I did-n't know, ex-cept you   give me some - thing   I can feel,

Riff A

1.

D5 E5 D5 E5 D5 E5 A5   Ab5 G5 D5 E5 D5 E5 D5 E5 A5   Ab5 G5

| / / / | / / / | / / / | / / / |:||

feel.   The

2.

A5   Ab5 G5

| / / / ||

Interlude

A G5* D* A   G5*   D A

| / / / | / / / | / / / | / / / |

G5*   D A

| / / / | / / / ||

Guitar solo

Riff A

D5 E5 D5 E5 D5 E5 A5   Ab5 G5 D5 E5 D5 E5 D5 E5 A5   Ab5 G5

| / / / | / / / | / / / | / / / |

Riff A

D5 E5 D5 E5 D5 E5 A5   Ab5 G5 D5 E5 D5 E5 D5 E5 A5   Ab5 G5

| / / / | / / / | / / / | / / / ||

Bridge

N.C. (E5)

| / / / | / / / | / / / | / / / |

All of this,   all of this can be yours.   All of this,   all of this can be yours.

                        N.C.

| / / / | / / / | / / / | / / / ||

All of this,   all of this can be yours. Just give me what I want   and no-one gets hurt.

Chorus

E   D   G5*   A5*

| / / / | / / / | / / / | / / / |

Hel-lo,   hel-lo,   ho-la! We're at a place called Ver-ti-go. *Don-de es*

E   D   G5*   A5*

| / / / | / / / | / / / | / / / |

Lights go down and   all I know is that you   give me some - thing I can

E   D   G5*   A5*

| / / / | / / / | / / / | / / / |

feel your love teach - ing me, ah.

E   D   G5*   A5*

| / / / | / / / | / / / | / / / |

Your love is teach - ing me, ah,   how to kneel,

Riff A

D5 E5 D5 E5 D5 E5 A5   Ab5 G5 D5 E5 D5 E5 D5 E5 A5   Ab5 G5

| / / / | / / / | / / / | / / / |

Riff A

                 kneel.

D5 E5 D5 E5 D5 E5 A5   Ab5 G5 D5 E5 D5 E5 D5 E5 A5   Ab5 G5

| / / / | / / / | / / / | / / / |

Yeah, yeah, yeah, yeah, yeah, yeah, yeah, yeah, yeah, yeah, yeah, yeah, yeah, yeah, yeah,

E*

| / / / ||

yeah.

WHISKEY IN THE JAR

Traditional. Arranged by Phil Lynott, Brian Downey & Eric Bell

C   G

saw Cap - tain Far - rell   and his mo - ney he was count - ting.   I
took all of his mo - ney   and I bought it home to Mol - ly.   She
tak - ing my mo - ney with me   and I nev - er knew the dan - ger.   For a -
some men like to hear   a can - non ball a roar - ing.

G   Em

first produced my pis - tol   and then pro - duced my ra - pier   I said
swore that she'd love me,   nev - er would she leave me.   But the
- bout six or may - be se - ven,   in walked Cap - tain Far - rell,   I jumped up,
Me I like sleep - ing   spe - cially in my Mol - lys cham - ber,

C   G

"Stand and de - li - ver   or the de - vil he may take ya."   Mush - a
de - vil take that wo - man,   for you know she tricked me ea - sy.
fired off my pis - tols,   and I shot him with both bar - rels.
but here I am in pri - son,   here I am with a ball and chain, yeah.

Chorus

D   C

ring dum - a - doo, dum - a - da.   Whack for my dad - dy - o,   *2° To Coda* ⊕   F

G

whack for my dad - dy - o,   there's whis - key in the jar - o.

Interlude

Riff A

Em   G   F

| 1, 3. |

Em   G

| 2. |

Guitar solo   % Now

G   Em

C   G

D   C

G   F

Interlude

Riff A

Em   G

Em   G   *D.S. al Coda (with repeat)*

⊕ *Coda*

Riff A

Em   G   *Repeat 4 times to fade*

Ad lib. Vx.

YOUTH GONE WILD

Words & Music by Rachel Bolan & Dave 'The Snake' Sabo

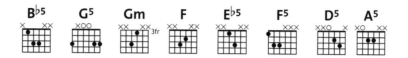

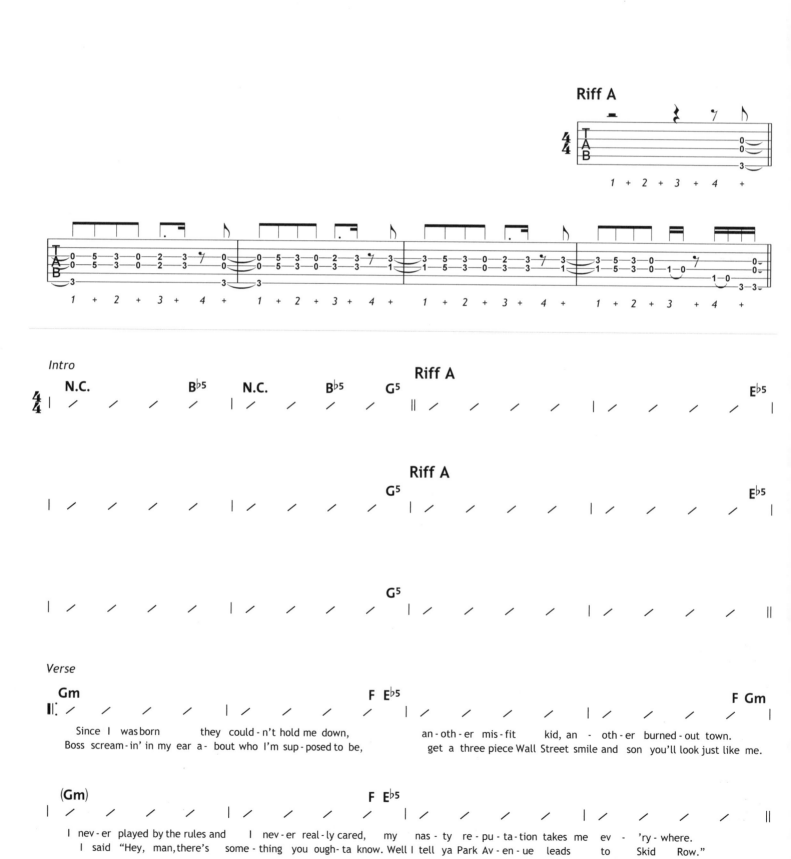

Intro

Verse

Since I was born   they could-n't hold me down,   an-oth-er mis-fit kid, an-oth-er burned-out town.
Boss scream-in' in my ear a-bout who I'm sup-posed to be,   get a three piece Wall Street smile and son you'll look just like me.

I nev-er played by the rules and   I nev-er real-ly cared,   my nas-ty re-pu-ta-tion takes me ev-'ry-where.
I said "Hey, man, there's   some-thing you ough-ta know. Well I tell ya Park Av-en-ue leads   to   Skid Row."

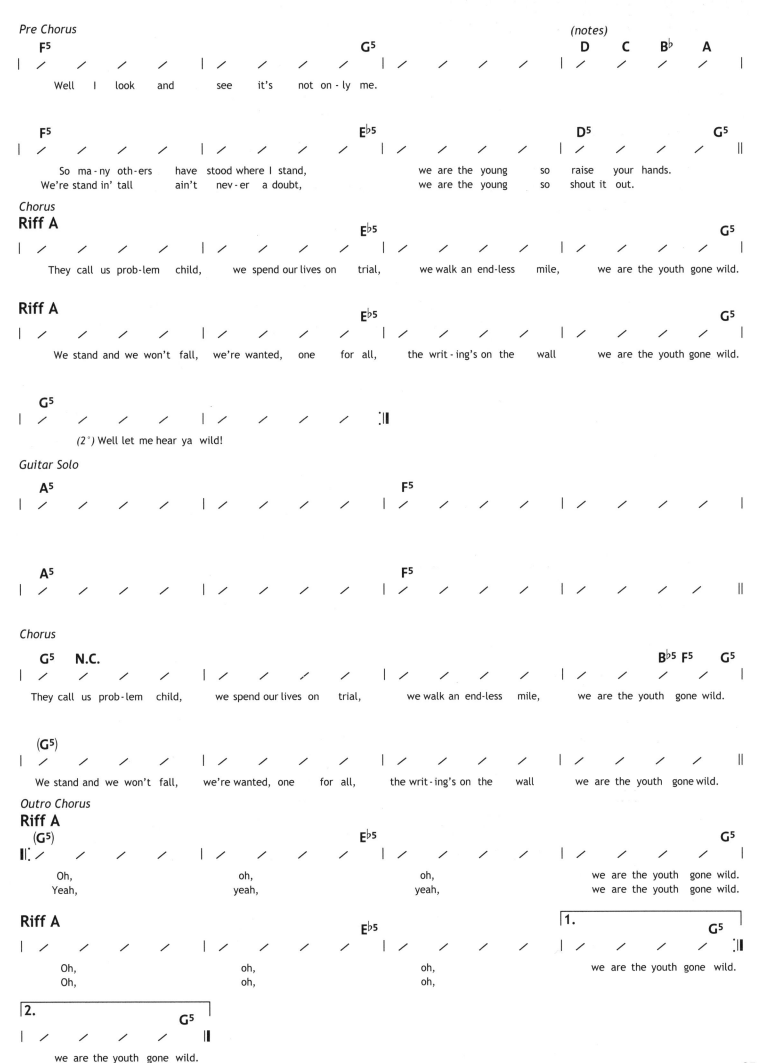

Pre Chorus

F5   G5   *(notes)*   D   C   B♭   A

Well I look and see it's not on - ly me.

F5   E♭5   D5   G5

So ma - ny oth-ers have stood where I stand,   we are the young so raise your hands.
We're stand in' tall ain't nev - er a doubt,   we are the young so shout it out.

Chorus
Riff A

                          E♭5   G5

They call us prob-lem child, we spend our lives on trial, we walk an end-less mile, we are the youth gone wild.

Riff A

                          E♭5   G5

We stand and we won't fall, we're wanted, one for all, the writ - ing's on the wall we are the youth gone wild.

G5

(2°) Well let me hear ya wild!

Guitar Solo

A5   F5

A5   F5

Chorus

G5   N.C.   B♭5 F5   G5

They call us prob-lem child,   we spend our lives on trial,   we walk an end-less mile,   we are the youth gone wild.

(G5)

We stand and we won't fall,   we're wanted, one for all,   the writ-ing's on the wall   we are the youth gone wild.

Outro Chorus
Riff A

(G5)   E♭5   G5

Oh,   oh,   oh,   we are the youth gone wild.
Yeah,   yeah,   yeah,   we are the youth gone wild.

Riff A

                      E♭5   **1.**   G5

Oh,   oh,   oh,   we are the youth gone wild.
Oh,   oh,   oh,

2.   G5

we are the youth gone wild.

HOW TO USE THIS BOOK

Each song in this book is accompanied by a short segment of guitar tablature giving you an authentic, distinctive feature: an intro, a riff, a strumming pattern, a rhythmic figure, or other musical 'catch-phrase' to make your performance flow.

Watch out for instructions within the music – usually 'Riff A' or similar – to tell you when to play the notated figure. Sometimes, where it's more useful, a suggested strumming or picking pattern is included that can be used throughout the song.

Tablature (or TAB) is a system of notation specific to the guitar, and giving instructions not easily written in conventional notation. As with standard notation, rhythmic values can be indicated with note-tails and, in this book, the beat-count is also included below the staff to make rhythms easier to read.

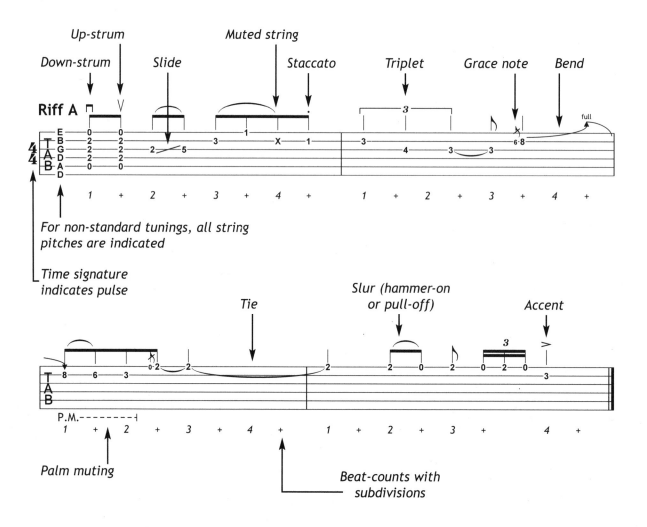